MW00628838

THE NEW HEALERS

The New Healers
HEALING THE WHOLE PERSON

Edited by
Larry Geis
and Alta Picchi Kelly, Ph.D.
with Aidan Kelly

A NEW DIMENSIONS SERIES BOOK

AND/OR PRESS, INC.   1980

Cover & text design: Bonnie Smetts
Cover photo: Patricia Fearey
Typesetting: Ann Flanagan Typography
Proofreading: Sayre Van Young

Cover calligraphy: Calligraphos

Copyright ©1980 the New Dimensions Foundation. All rights reserved, including the right to reproduce this book or portions thereof in any form whatsoever, except for use by a reviewer in connection with a review.

Published and distributed by: And/Or Press
                              P.O. Box 2246
                              Berkeley, CA 94702

ISBN: 0-915904-49-7

Printed in the United States of America

First printing March 1980

CONTENTS

PREFACE

HEALTH: A state of being we each relate to in our own way. Usually, we don't think too much about it unless it's not there. Many of us see health as the absence of disease or pain; yet the dictionary's first given meaning of health is, "the condition of being sound in body, mind, or spirit."

Modern health care, with its emphasis on technology, has focused on the body as the key to good health, with mind and spirit considered more or less as afterthoughts. In this book you will come in touch with modern-day healers who see body, mind, and spirit as integral parts of a contiguous whole, each as important as the other.

Another equally important theme presented here is the responsibility we each have for our own health. We cannot expect doctors, therapists, druggists, or public officials to take the full responsibility for making us well through visits, hospitalizations, pills, or laws. Even though medical technology has reached its most sophisticated state and has provided many solutions to health problems, individual health has not flourished as expected. The time is now—we each need to look to ourselves and to meet our equal responsibility in the domain of our personal health. To the extent that we each do this, the health of our society as a whole will improve. The solutions are not external—they are within. As we move toward reviewing our relationship with the medical and health-care professional and see them as partners in our wellness, we can also begin to refocus on health, not illness. The entire society will benefit as a result.

The themes expressed within the pages of this book first emerged through New Dimensions radio programming. When listeners hear our radio programs or audio tapes, they enter a realm without limits, where possibilities can be explored in all their depth and richness. By picking up this book and reading it, you have begun an adventure where you can discover the infinite panorama of possibilities available to you as a human being. Through this book we are able to expand our playground to encompass you, the reader. Welcome to our version of the ultimate journey, your own self-discovery. Enjoy.

Many people contributed to bringing this book into being. The original interviews from which most of these articles have been edited were done by Re Couture, Will Noffke, and Michael Toms. The transcribing was accomplished beyond our expectations by Phil Eversoul, Eric Snyder, Michelle Christides, Shera Thompson, and Charmaine Silverstein. Considerable technical support was given generously by Byron Hayes, Stephen Hill, Anna Turner, Phil Catalfo, Tom Greenaway, Ron Kemper, Lou Judson, and Dan Drasin. I especially need to thank: Peter Beren, for spearheading the project and seeing that it got done; Larry Geis, for selecting and assembling the primary materials for the book; Alta Picchi Kelly, Ph.D., for doing the final selection and organization of the materials, and for her insightful essays that introduce each section and chapter in the book; and Aidan A. Kelly, for his meticulous editing. I also want to thank all the New Dimensions staff members and other friends, too numerous to mention by name, who contributed all the same.

This book emerged from a vision of how the world can be a better place to live and how each of us contributes to making it so. For supporting that vision in every way, I thank my partner and wife, Justine Toms.

Michael A. Toms
Founding Director
New Dimensions Foundation

1 BASICS OF HOLISTIC HEALTH

WHO ARE THE NEW HEALERS, and what do they represent for health? We share with you a survey of the holistic health field, in the form of a selected overview of the concepts and personal experiences of famous healing practitioners. These doctors and healers have come to their work from diverse backgrounds. They approach health from different focuses, but they do hold in common certain ideas that govern how they practice the healing arts. The common themes that run through their articles are:

That Western scientific medicine has reached a high degree of technological advancement, but has drawbacks and limitations in working with chronic degenerative disease and with lifestyle problems;

That people are solely responsible for their own state of health;

That each person is a unique animal whose body, mind, and spirit work in harmony to produce well-being;

That health is a reminder of the quality of life we are living;

That no system, formula, or remedy of healing will work for everyone;

That no single practitioner of healing can treat all forms of disease;

3

That love underlies all techniques of healing and health.

Holistic health consists of enabling good health to emerge from within the person. Disease is seen as an important feedback message to be worked upon within the context of the whole life. The body knows best how to heal itself, if we can learn how to reduce stress and life problems.

Life is seen as including birth to death. Aging and childbirth are seen as part of the natural, normal cycle of life, not as disease or as anything in need of treatment. The object of holistic health is to develop a joyful expression of positive wellness within a system of self-responsibility.

"The Holistic View," by Richard B. Miles, an early participant in humanistic medicine and holistic-health care, discusses the history of holistic health, and the differences between the holistic approach and other forms of practice, to give us a better understanding of the current state and the future potential of holistic health.

Harold H. Bloomfield, M.D., in his article, "Designing Your Own Holistic Health Program," offers his insights into the rapidly changing ideas about a system of personal health care. His plan for working toward a feeling of optimal well-being covers the major areas of holistic health in relationship to the Body/Mind/Spirit. He shares with us his thoughts that change offers both an opportunity and a responsibility.

Both men share with us their personal experiences and points of view about this rapidly developing field.

A.P.K.

1 THE HOLISTIC VIEW
Richard B. Miles, Ph.D.

Hundreds of millions of dollars and hundreds of thousands of hours are spent each year in the pursuit of health after disease is already present in the body. *Yet health remains an elusive goal, not fully understood or achieved by most people.*

Western medicine has tended to define health as the absence of symptoms of disease. In this perspective, little action to affect health can be taken until symptoms appear. In addition, since the development of the "germ theory" of disease in the late 1800s, symptoms are generally assumed to be caused by invading agents. Although remarkably successful for combatting infectious diseases, this perspective is essentially inadequate for dealing with chronic, degenerative disease, which is the main concern of the present health-care situation.

A new breed of healers is now looking beyond the current system of allopathic medicine. These men and women look at illness in terms of a continuum which moves from imminent death on the left, through normalcy (the absence of symptoms) at the center, to "high-level wellness" as an achievable goal on the right.

High-level wellness can be achieved only by means of the personal awareness and participation of the individual who recognizes that attitudes, stress, nutrition, and exercise all affect the level of well-being, and chooses to do something positive about them.

Our views of health and illness have evolved as our society has changed its view of humanity and the world. In physics, chemistry, biology, and other sciences, significant changes have developed in "worldview" theories since the turn of the century. As our scientists explore the universe, and our understanding shifts, our perspective on life, health, and disease also changes.

A review of these changes and of new ways to look at health and disease is offered here by Richard B. Miles, an early pioneer in the holistic-health movement. Starting with a major acupuncture symposium in May 1972, Dr. Miles developed and staged "The Dimensions of Healing" in 1972-1973, "Frontiers of the Mind" in 1973-74, and other conferences and seminars on new perspectives in health. He was a founding director of the Holistic Health Institute in San Francisco. In 1978, Richard chaired the Menninger Foundation's Council Grove Conference, an annual forum of leaders in new healing. With Arthur Kaslow, M.D., of Santa Barbara, Richard authored Freedom From Chronic Disease *(Los Angeles; Tarcher, 1979), an explanation of a self-healing approach to systemic disorders. He teaches "Fundamentals of Holistic Health" in the Health Science Department of San Jose State University, and is a member of the faculty of the General Studies Program at John F. Kennedy University in Orinda, California.*

"HOLISTIC HEALTH" MEANS different things to different people. Sometimes the term is used to describe a collection of modalities or methods of healing, which presumably are more holistic than traditional allopathic medicine. The term is also used by health-education centers which feel they are essentially directed toward, and responsive to, the health needs of their clients.

I feel the term represents a change in the views in the society, a change much larger and more basic than either of these descriptions would imply. Holistic health is no less than a new way that our society is looking at humanity and the world.

If we look at the frontiers of physics and biology, at the changing views of ecology, we see that society is reevaluating a number of basic assumptions about our relationship with nature and our relationships with one another. Science's views in most of these fields are becoming more holistic.

In order to define "holistic," we must look at its counterpart: the traditional, reductionistic, scientific view of this culture. In the reductionistic approach, we take things apart and categorize them; we break them down into their smallest parts and list the parts. Then we assume that we can take all those parts and assemble them into some kind of whole, and that, by doing so, we will have an understanding of how nature works, and how various biological processes work.

The holistic approach, however, finds that the whole is greater than the sum of its parts. There is some essence, some energy, or

Christopher Wentworth

*Richard
Miles*

some life force involved in the biological process which cannot be perceived simply by adding up all the parts. Imagine one of those elaborate 5,000-piece jigsaw puzzles, where all the pieces are about the same size and look a lot alike. Imagine dumping it out on a table and trying to assemble the puzzle without having the picture on the box. It would be a very tedious, difficult process. That's analogous to the process we've used to look at the world in the reductionist, Aristotelian, Cartesian view. We look out at the world and we observe what is there, and from that hopefully honest observation, we attempt to build a sense of how the world works. The holistic thinker, on the other hand, is not satisfied with that approach. He or she needs a vision of the desirable outcome, a vision of the whole, a picture of how everything fits together.

Medical Models and Systems

Our view of how everything fits together in this culture has changed significantly in the last six or seven hundred years. The original view in our culture, based on the Judaeo-Christian tradition, centered around the concept of a great director in the sky with long flowing white hair, sitting on the big chair. Events on the Earth were essentially the result of the plan of this One God. Our role down here was to find out what that plan was and to make some attempt to be obedient to it. Given this perspective of the world, disease and ill health became connected with shame and guilt and sin. We thought that if we experienced ill health or if some epidemic or natural event caused disease, we must have done something that offended God in some way. We still find a lot of this kind of thinking in primitive cultures: God must somehow be appeased in order to achieve health and societal well-being.

Implicit in that traditional perspective was the concept of perfection. God was perfect. Somehow we were to try to achieve that perfection by obedience to God, thereby achieving what was known as "a state of grace." Perfection has always been very difficult to define. Ask a bunch of people on the street to define perfection for you, and you quickly get into a lively discussion of divergent meanings. Consequently, caught in a system that demanded perfection, but being unable to define it adequately, about all we could do was to go to the other side of the coin and identify and correct specific things when they went wrong. Somehow we seemed to know when things went wrong. We knew when we were ill, and we knew when things didn't seem to be right with us. Take a look at our culture and you quickly see that we put a lot of energy into the identification and correction of error. We wait for things to go wrong, and then try to figure out how to fix them. Along came the Renaissance and the Reformation, with the burst of thinking that resulted in new and different philosophies. As the Protestant sects were formed, each tried to come up with its own definition of perfection, which differed somewhat from the Roman Catholic version.

Then modern empirical science began to observe the world objectively in the laboratory. Science came up with a new yardstick for measuring the human condition: normalcy, or the bell-shaped curve. This new yardstick is more or less superimposed on the old Judaeo-Christian ethic. In this model, health is normalcy, rather than perfection. If we study a thousand people to determine what health is, whatever the majority of those people are exhibiting is defined as "health" in the normalcy system.

There is a kind of tyranny implicit in the normalcy viewpoint. Carl Jung said normalcy is the force that creates mental illness. When one is trying to be normal, but can't really understand what normal means, there is a tremendous pressure to conform, to be like everyone else. There isn't any real way to figure what you're supposed to be or how to be healthy. In the normalcy system, disease is simply deviation from the norm. If there's a statistical analysis of some particular health problem, those who deviate from the norm are considered to be in ill health.

In the early part of this century, laboratory science developed the germ-theory medical model in the United States. If we became ill, it was because a little creature, a bacterium or a virus or a bacillus, had invaded our body. If we could identify this creature, and either remove it from the body or affect it with chemicals, the body would no longer have to contend with it, and we would become well again. That was largely true for the infectious diseases that were the primary problem of the physician in the 1910s and 1920s: tuberculosis, diphtheria, smallpox, pneumonia, poliomylitis, etc. Older people can still remember the kind of fears these infectious diseases used to raise. The germ-theory model of treatment was so successful against these diseases that some younger physicians may never have encountered them in their practice.

Today, the main issues in medicine are the chronic, degenerative diseases: cancer, arthritis, cardiovascular disorders, neuromuscular failures, chronic pain, alcohol and drug abuse. These problems do not arise because some identifiable entity has entered the body. Rather, they result from degeneration of the self-regulation processes of the body. Consequently, the prevailing medical system, relying on pharmaceuticals and surgery, has been ineffective in dealing with these diseases.

Some "cures" for degenerative diseases, such as radiation treatment and chemotherapy for cancer, and cortisone injections for arthritis, create as much pain and stress for the person as the disease itself. If you believe that medical science must attack disease with chemicals and/or surgery, you may have to damage or kill a fairly significant portion of the body that is experiencing the disease in order to rid the person of the disease. That's a pretty aggressive position.

Along with this, there is a rising public expectation about the future success of medicine. Since medicine was so successful in dealing with the infectious diseases, we created the omnipotent hero-doctor. Society began to expect that medical science could simply fix everything. And this trend continues, with a rising expectation among the public of quick success in the treatment of disease, and a falling success rate for the medical profession. There is disenchantment and misunderstanding on both sides. The medical profession has continued to become more specialized and discrete, while the diseases have become more general and more a part of everyday life.

Out of this ferment has come what is now called the holistic-health movement. The movement has several aspects. One of these is the use of alternative modalities for treatment. Some of these modalities—acupuncture, meditation, such body-energy systems as shiatzu massage—have been imported from the East. Others—biofeedback, Rolfing, bioenergetics—have emerged in the West. Almost all these new modalities approach the human body as an operating system rather than as a site for attack by disease. Healing is seen as restoring the function of the system, not as a fixing of symptoms.

Along with this sudden rash of new modalities and new ways of looking at the body, there's also a change in the valuc system. As Joseph Chilton Pearce points out in his book *Exploring the Crack in the Cosmic Egg,* one of the basic assumptions of our technological culture is that nature is an adversary. Western science and literature are filled with references to man's need to master the forces of nature. The assumption is that if we fail to learn how to manipulate the processes of nature, such as the weather, agricultural systems, and the chemical workings of our bodies, then nature will "get us" and we won't survive on this planet. Such a perspective is unique to technological cultures, and is not necessarily shared by other cultures. The ecology movement, the natural-foods movement, the physical-fitness movement, all question that assumption. It may be that nature is a fairly wise system that we have misunderstood.

Along with a new perspective that nature is our friend, we

may find that disease can also be our friend. If we are in a natural system that is meant to support human existence and human expression, then we have to come to some new understanding of the role of illness. Perhaps we can't make it an enemy to attack or an abnormalcy to be removed. It must have some reason for being there, some purpose in the natural system.

Cancer

Some researchers are contending that the causes of cancer can be traced back to environmental pollution of some sort or another. Most of these environmental carcinogens have been put into our social existence by technology. We put a lot of lead and carbon monoxide in the air. We add chemicals to food. We put chemicals into the soil to try to boost agricultural production. We use pesticides, which also wind up in our food. Some 3,500 apparent carcinogens have been identified. The majority of them are manufactured products rather than things which would occur naturally in the environment. As we, at our own risk, create an environment that is not natural, we should realize the body may not have appropriate immune systems to defend against it.

There are, of course, people in the environs of those carcinogens who don't seem to get cancer. There seem to be strong links between cancer and certain lifestyle stresses. Dr. Carl Simonton, in his work in Ft. Worth, Texas, has noted that about 85 per cent of the advanced cancer patients he works with have suffered some significant emotional trauma. The trauma may be the loss of a loved one, the loss of a career position, or some other significant shift in life. This type of person just doesn't see how to make it any more; there is a loss of the will to live. We may find that people who are exposed to certain carcinogens and who also have certain lifestyle stresses or emotional issues in their lives may be the ones who are most susceptible to cancer.

Feedback Systems

Our society has a tendency to look for the *one* answer to everything. Because we found the one cause of pneumonia, the one cause of tuberculosis, and the one cause of smallpox, now we're looking for the one cause for cancer or the one cause for arthritis. It may be that in these body-process diseases we're looking at combinations of factors; so it would be difficult to track • down that *one* creature we're supposed to try to eliminate.

I assume we as human beings are choosing creatures, that we have some role to play in the definition of our own destiny. We are not simply cast into life to be buffeted by the seas and the winds. We choose a lot of the events in our lives, and we set up our lives in certain ways to create certain effects. This choosing system we all use has certain feedback processes built into it, similar to those of computer systems. A gyroscopic compass or an automatic pilot in an airplane are good examples of that. Built into the system is feedback information about the winds, the course, and other data; so that if the plane begins to get off-course, that information comes back to the central control computer and is processed, and the course correction is made. The human body employs similar feedback loops. We have highly sensitive nervous and endocrine systems that are constantly feeding information back to the brain to tell the person what's going on in the body. Since we are self-choosing systems, we need feedback information when things are not working right.

From that perspective, disease can be seen as an internal feedback mechanism. Let's say that we're working too hard, and encountering a lot of stress in our work at the office. Lo and behold, after a week or two of that we get a cold. We just don't feel we can handle it any more. Now we have a reason to take a day or two off and spend the time in bed resting and taking care of ourselves. The cold acts as a message, which says, "Slow down, take it easy. Your body is tired. You need to recoup."

The message can be even more specific than that. For instance, on TV we constantly see images that represent the three main health issues in our country: sinus trouble and colds; tension headaches; and upset stomachs. (Of course, anyone who watches TV knows that the commercials may themselves create tension headaches and upset stomachs.) Looking at the way we behave in our culture, we can find certain kinds of behavior that are very difficult for us to display in public or even in the privacy of our families. One of these is crying. Most people in our culture do not feel comfortable crying anywhere. Look at the symptoms of a cold. All the physiological reactions associated with a cold are the same as crying: tearing of the eyes, congestion in the sinus passages, and a heated, flushed feeling. There may be a message to us in the common cold that we are suppressing something. It may be something we are sad about or something we are upset about, something we need to express. But we don't feel we have permission to express it; so we come down with a cold as a convenient way of allowing our body to express that emotion.

Cancer as Faulty Feedback

Cancer is one of two conditions. It may be a conflict within the body, a process in the body that is not in harmony with the rest of the natural processes of the body. Cancer is a division of cells that produces a growth mechanism alien to the rest of the cell development in the body. Cancer, therefore, may be seen as conflict disease.

Or cancer may be viewed as an identity crisis. The system that monitors unwanted material in the body is the lymphocytes in the bloodstream. These white blood cells travel around acting like watchdogs, saying, "This is a friendly substance; or this is an unfriendly substance." The material in the bloodstream is identified in terms of whether it is compatible with the normal processes going on in the body. The identity code is apparently built into the DNA structure of each individual. If that identity code is thrown into doubt, then the watchdog running through the bloodstream becomes confused about what is friendly and what is not friendly. Some types of leukemia seem to be diseases of confusion, where white blood cells multiply profusely and attack everything that comes by. In other types of cancer, the white blood cells don't seem to attack anything. Therefore there is some confusion about what is a foreign entity and what belongs in that body.

A physician in Sunset Beach, California, who is both a gynecologist and a psychiatrist saw a number of woman patients who had cancer of the cervix or cancer of the breast. In his psychiatric work with these patients, he found that a high percentage of the women had a lot of unexpressed anger toward their spouses. They did not feel permission to express this hidden anger. Perhaps the husbands spent too much time at work or didn't allow them enough money or whatever. At any rate, the women felt dominated by the husbands and unable to express this anger. When this issue of conflict was confronted in the psychiatric work with the patients and their husbands, some of the cancers began to remit. In other words, once the women got in touch with the conflict and saw that they might even be using their disease to deny their husbands access to their sexual favors, then the whole situation around the disease changed. Suddenly they didn't need cancer any more. That may sound very esoteric and mysterious, but all I am saying is that disease does have some function as a message back to the person who's experiencing the disease.

Dr. Breisser in Los Angeles did a study of his patients who were diagnosed to have cancer or other life-threatening illnesses. Some of these individuals, when diagnosed as having cancer, were so affronted by the idea that they simply refused to believe it. They went about their business, and said, "I'm not going to be treated, and I'm not going to go through with this. I'm simply not going to have this happen in my life. I don't want it." An extremely high percentage of these people remitted the disease, much to the doctor's great surprise. It would seem that the mindset or the self-image of the individual apparently is a large factor in cancer.

Attitudes and Assumptions

If people can stop and take a look at what is going on in their lives and in their body processes when they begin to experience some illness or upset, perhaps they can get in touch with what that might mean to them. I believe that could be a very significant factor in the development of their own healing. However, I don't want to suggest that if you are diagnosed as having cancer or some other serious illness, you simply go off and sit in a chair somewhere or work with a counselor in order to figure out what the disease means to you, and that would be the extent of what you do about it. We should all have all the choices available to us that medical science or other new modalities can offer. The individual should be able to choose what he or she would like to do about it. Many people might not have the will power or the self-actualizing ability needed to deal with the fear and anxiety that a life-threatening disease may create. Therefore they may want to seek medical treatment, and use the medical techniques, such as

surgery or chemotherapy, available to them. I don't want to give
the impression that we in the holistic-health field ridicule traditional medicine and say that it has no value. I think it's a question
of the person getting the disease into perspective and then using
those processes that are available in the wisest possible way.

NBC television, in a recent show reviewing the current state
of medical art, talked about the four consumer assumptions about
medical care. The first assumption is that doctors can fix
anything. The second assumption is that nobody personally pays
for medical care, because insurance companies and government
programs take care of the bill. The third assumption is that doctors will always give one the best treatment that is available,
which means that a person from a small town will be rushed to
the big medical center in the city and be hooked to the most
sophisticated equipment. Finally, it is assumed that any amount
of money should be spent to rescue a person from imminent
death. These four assumptions point to the cause of skyrocketing
medical costs.

It is estimated that 80 per cent of the money that an average
person spends on medical care is spent in the last two years of
life. If that's true, it means we are spending huge amounts of
money trying to rescue people in their later years from the ex-
cesses of their earlier years. I doubt we can continue to spend
that kind of money on this immense rescue system. I don't think
the public will continue to support it.

On a more positive side, there is a growing public awareness
of the factors in our lifestyles that are causing a lot of these
serious medical problems. Many heart problems, arthritis problems, strokes, and so forth are directly related to the way we live.
As people become more aware of these causes and change their
lifestyles accordingly, I think the use of our traditional medical
system will begin to diminish. There is an interesting reason for
this: our American medical system actually has the least control
over its constituency of any of the institutions in our culture. For
instance, if I don't want my kids attending public schools, it's a
very expensive major effort to set up some other kind of educational process for them. If I want to go out and buy an automobile
or a blender, I've got to buy them from the dealers that sell them
and the companies that make them. Most industries and professional institutions in this culture have this kind of direct link to

their constituency. But in the health-care system, if I can devise some process that I think is more beneficial to my health than going to see a doctor, there isn't any reason why I have to go see a doctor.

Facing the Fact of Death

In our allopathic medical system, the function of the physician is to identify and correct error. If he is successful and the patient returns to health, he is a hero, because this devastating thing that is happening goes away. Now, obviously the most devastating thing that can happen to the patient is death. Consequently, the physician must look upon the death of any patient as a personal failure. It's very difficult for a patient in a hospital who has been diagnosed as having a terminal condition, because he then becomes almost an outcast in the hospital. Nobody wants to talk to him, nobody wants to relate to him, nobody wants to "share his space," so to speak, because most medical people view him as a failure, someone that they could not rescue. Failure disturbs these professionals emotionally; consequently, they withdraw from that patient. It may turn out that this withdrawal syndrome is one of the main causes of death in our culture.

Let's also look at how our culture avoids risk. We don't like to take risk. We want security; we want things to be calm, even, and predictable. And the greatest risk of all is death. So, obviously we avoid death at all costs. We don't want to talk about it. We don't want to have it in our presence. We take the older folks who are suffering from physical difficulties and put them in what we used to call convalescent hospitals, which is really a bad joke, since few of them leave until they die. Now we call them long-term care facilities or some other kind of euphemism. We put our old people away, so that we won't have to interact with them, so that we won't have to look at oncoming death.

However, our perspective on death is changing. People like Charles Garfield and Elisabeth Kubler-Ross are looking at the whole process of death in order to remove the stigma. We can change our values and our views about the transition experience, so that we can relate to dying people, so that we can be with them and comfort them and share with them.

If the people in the health profession can begin to accept death as part of a natural process, then a lot of the expensive rescue heroics and artificial life-extension processes will become unnecessary. If they can simply relate to the patient at the appropriate level of disease experience, it may be perfectly acceptable for the patient to die, with no fear or resistance on either side. Especially in advanced years, a lot of people simply don't want to have to undergo the stress and torment of being a vegetable in the hospital for months on end, of being a burden on their family, all the things that are associated with those long illnesses. Our system is so afraid to allow them to die. The doctor is afraid of being accused of failing, and the system is afraid of being accused of being heartless. These fears may not be relevant factors at all. It's just a question of how we look at these life processes.

Being healthy implies an assumption that one is doing something productive and fulfilling, something one feels good about. One is not in conflict with the body, not in conflict with family and associates, not in conflict with nature. Things are progressing in a fulfilling, creative cycle. Therein lies a paradox or two. A number of noted people in the history of our culture whom we consider very creative, like Leonardo da Vinci and Winston Churchill and Mozart, were not people whom we would always call mentally or physically healthy. A person who is fulfilled by pursuing exactly what he or she intends to pursue may live only to 35 and die of some bizarre disease. Perhaps that is okay for that person; perhaps that's what he or she would like to have happen. We all put a lot of value judgments on these things because we all want to live to be a hundred, we all want to have beautiful physiques, and we all want to be sexually attractive. The irony is that this value set of our culture doesn't seem to make very many people happy. People are reevaluating these values, asking, "What is it inside me that I need to do?"

2 DESIGNING YOUR OWN HOLISTIC HEALTH PROGRAM

Harold H. Bloomfield, M.D.

Harold H. Bloomfield, M.D., Director of Psychiatry at the North County Holistic Health Center in Del Mar, California, completed his psychiatric training at the Yale University School of Medicine. He is a member of the American Psychiatric Association and a founding member of the Association for Holistic Health. He is Professor of Holistic Health and Humanistic Psychology at the University for Humanistic Studies in San Diego. His books include TM: Discovering Inner Energy and Overcoming Stress; How to Survive the Loss of Love; Happiness: The TM Program, Psychiatry, and Enlightenment. *He has lectured worldwide on the "Mastery of Stress," "The Expansion of Happiness," and "The Development of Full Human Potential." His newest books are* The Holistic Way to Health and Happiness: A New Approach to Complete Lifetime Wellness, *and* How to Enjoy the Love of Your Life.

As Harold Bloomfield says, "You have a center for holistic health that has been within you all the time, waiting for you to move in and develop your potential to the maximum." His approach to holistic health is broad and challenging. He believes in change through self responsibility, discipline, and moderation.

In the following article, Dr. Bloomfield covers a wide variety of holistic-health techniques and principles that work toward optimal health. His approach to well-being covers the mind, body, spirit, and environment.

EVEN THOUGH DOCTORS WILL HAVE to remain specialists in disease management, you can design and implement a health pro-

courtesy of M. Bloomfield

*Harold
Bloomfield*

gram that is best for you. Here I am going to give you an overview of what consistencies to look for in becoming your own
health expert.

The New Perspective

Now that I see myself as a holistic psychiatrist, I no longer
think of myself as being a "shrink," but as a "stretch." I actively
advocate stretching body, mind, and spirit as much as possible.
We need to expand our human potential; we have had enough
shrinking of it. Despite our tremendous affluence, we find our
health has actually been deteriorating. These days 80 per cent of
the patients who come to general practitioners have no definable
organic illness. They are suffering from the symptoms of stress,
such as excessive fatigue, low back pain, gastrointestinal complaints, and just not feeling good. Too many of us have gotten

used to seeing that as a normal part of life. For many of us, the best we can do seems to be just living with our bad health habits. We have to set a new vision, a new direction, a new goal. We have to cultivate our own optimal health, positive wellness, self-actualization, and enlightenment, however we want to conceptualize it. As we do so, the problems, the negativities, are going to start to fall away.

The major message of holistic health is *responsibility*. The word "responsibility" sometimes sounds a little too puritanical to me. It reminds me of the old attitudes that you *have* to brush your teeth every morning, you *have* to do your exercises, you have *got* to meditate, etc. I like to think of health as your opportunity. Health and happiness go together. We have to find a way to make health joyful, not tedious. We can do it in a gradual, systematic process, which will be a lot less expensive to us economically as well as in terms of our health.

In the last five years in this country, we have spent five billion dollars on health care, but only about 2.5 per cent of that has gone to education and prevention. It is really quite remarkable that we spend 97 per cent of our health funds on treatment, with 50 per cent of that going to the end stages of heart disease, cancer, and lung problems. I think we have to rearrange our priorities a little bit, not give up any of the modern medical miracles that we have developed, but get more training, so that we can develop our own health potential. At this point only about 6 per cent of our population, according to some studies, is living anywhere near optimal health. One third of our population suffers from chronic disabilities, because over the years we have been systematically violating certain health laws of nature. If you make mistakes, after a while nature is going to give you a little slap. But if you start to go along with nature, pay attention, and enjoy that flow of effortless naturalness coming through you, you start to enjoy higher and higher levels of being and wellness.

The Holistically Healthy Person

The holistically healthy person is an individual (I say "he" in this list only because continually saying "he or she" would get clumsy) who is trim, physically fit, full of energy, and vigorous.

He rarely gets tired, and if he does, he usually knows what to do about it: he gets some rest.

He is free from minor complaints, such as indigestion, constipation, headaches, or insomnia. He feels good as a baseline.

He is alert, able to concentrate, and clear-headed. A lot of us get used to feeling foggy sometimes or not able to concentrate. We should have our minds in a state of restful alertness as a baseline.

He is radiant, especially his skin, hair, and eyes.

He is active and creative. We all are highly creative people. We have to put our energy to work. We all have tremendous potentials not only to enjoy ourselves, but also to share with one another. That is part of being holistically healthy.

He is able to relax easily, and is free from anxiety and worry. That is the real key: stress reduction is very important. He is self-assured, confident, and optimistic. I see optimism, by the way, as the human baseline. Being optimistic and being realistic, to me, go hand and hand.

He is satisfied with his work and with the direction of his life.

He is able to assert himself, to stand up for his rights.

He is satisfied with his sexual relationships. Being able to have a full degree of pleasure in your life, including the sexual and love areas, is extremely important.

He is free from destructive health habits, such as smoking, overeating, and excessive drinking. If we are going to become holistically healthy, we are going to have to give up those cigarettes. The key to giving up negative health habits is to concentrate on making some positive changes. Take up meditation, TM, jogging, or psychocalisthenics, and develop a lifestyle where you get more pleasure from exercise, meditating, and enjoying life than from smoking cigarettes, and you will find out that the cigarette doesn't taste good any more, that you don't *want* it.

The individual who is holistically healthy is also able to respond to the challenges in life as opportunities to grow rather than as problems. He is able to create the life that he really wants, rather than just react to what seems to happen. He is able to enjoy a sense of well-being amidst adversity, of being fulfilled and at a peace with himself, able to enjoy his own life, and contribute to the lives of others.

How are we to reach this goal of becoming holistically

healthy and living this high road of wellness? For one thing we need to approach it as a total person rather than piecemeal.

The Holistic Approach to Dieting

It amazes me that if we want to lose weight, we think we just need a diet. Someone told me that if you want to sell a lot of books, write a diet book. There are billions of diet books sold all the time, and clearly they haven't done much good at all. The waistline seems to be expanding along with the wallets of the people who write the diet books, because the problem can't be solved merely by a diet alone. We need a holistic approach.

First of all, a holistic approach is feeling good about yourself, not getting into low self-esteem. You have to have high self-esteem to make some changes. You can't be downgrading yourself if you are in the process of losing weight.

Second, you need to develop more inner harmony. As you begin a stress-reduction program by taking up meditation or whatever helps you cultivate some inner silence, you start to get in touch with your *appestat,* your inner voice that says "Harold, you are getting full," or "Joan, maybe that food isn't so good for you." Once you start getting in touch with what is right for you, it works in every area of your life. Not only are you aware of when you are full and ready to leave the table, but you start to feel a need to exercise, because you are in touch with your body. Your muscles want to take you out for a walk, and they won't leave you alone until you go. Your inner health authority also tells you when you are sexually turned on and when you are not. It tells you when you are really in love, when a person in a relationship is right for you, and when he or she isn't.

It is amazing, when you start getting in touch with yourself, how many mistakes you can avoid, and how much more joy in life you can have for yourself. Nature built in those inner mechanisms, but stress clouds them over; so stress reduction is an important key, because we reduce our worry and our depression. Then, in a very natural way, we can start losing weight because we are enjoying our bodies more.

As this process continues, we engage in a fitness program: we start to run more, swim more, bicycle more, and our image

It is amazing how many foods have sugar in them. I have gone through the shock of walking down the aisle, of the super-market, starting to read some labels, and becoming aghast at how much sugar is hidden in products. In order to reduce the amount of sugar you are consuming, you have to start reading labels. Again, I'm not fanatical about it; but I use much less food that has hidden sugar. For instance, I am now careful to buy catsup that doesn't have sugar added. Lots of health-food stores have such catsups. I don't use salad dressings that are bought in stores. I do my own oil and vinegar, and avoid the added sugars.

I have also cut out soft drinks entirely. The research coming out on the potentially adverse affects of saccharin makes it much easier for me not even think about soft drinks, either with or without sugar. If I need a drink, I now enjoy good water. If you are lucky enough to have good water in your area, fine, otherwise you have to bring it in bottled. Or if you want something else, there is nothing like fresh orange juice or apple juice or, even bet-ter, a piece of fruit.

We also need to cut down on salt, another ingredient hidden in foods. The average American needs only about one-quarter gram of salt a day; yet we consume ten grams of salt a day, forty times more then we need. You can imagine what that does to the poor old kidneys. I remember learning in medical school that we need only 5 per cent of one kidney to survive on. I wondered why nature gives us that much leeway; now I understand why.

What is most important for nutrition is eating foods that are natural and wholesome, that are as close as possible to the way that God, in all his supreme wisdom, presented them to us from the earth or the tree for us to enjoy. If we get back to cultivating our own natural attunement to what is good for us, and start eating more natural foods without all that processing and chemicals, we will get into much more holistic living.

Stress Reduction

You need to find out what program of stress reduction is right for you. My own experience has been with the TM program. I have loved it and gotten a lot out of it, as have many others, but for some it has been less than wonderful. Investigate and find out what form of meditation or relaxation, of cultivating what we call the "healing silence," allows your mind to settle down and do its psychological housecleaning. I see Mother or Father Nature during this time sort of dusting up here and there, and tidying up the cobwebs in our minds. We need that for about 15 or 20 minutes a day; it is very, very important.

Self-Responsibility

Earlier I touched on the general concept of being responsible for your physical health. A related concept is to be responsible for your own mental health, to develop your emotions, to restructure your programming. We have all inherited an incredible amount of negative programming from the process of growing up—the can'ts, shouldn'ts, mustn'ts. We need to free ourselves from all that, so that we can love more, grow more, give more, and find out that we can skip down the street. Who says you can't get up and do some stretching exercises at the office for a few minutes if you are feeling tight? Who says that you can't take the phone off the hook for 20 minutes so that you can do some meditation? Who says that women can't say to men, "Hey, I would really like to spend some time with you"? Who says that a man can't say "No"? Let's share the risks. We have to develop our intrapersonal and interpersonal confidence.

Learning how to become competent in handling our anger and sharing our love and getting over our fears with one another is important. We need to avail ourselves of the educational programs that are available for this kind of learning. This learning process is different for each of us; so you have to investigate carefully to find out which program is right for you. The "human technology" is there to help us grow at an incredible rate, and make amazing changes in our personality and in the way we live.

This rapid growth results from a combination of two things: (1) insight into what has been going on and understanding what we want to change; and (2) focusing in and making the behavioral changes. I have observed, both personally and as a psychiatrist, that often insight can come *later*. You can make the behavioral change and get over the "I can't do it"; you can start exercising; you can start developing your emotional relationships; and *then* you will get an insight into what was blocking you from doing that in the first place. Both the insight and the behavioral change are needed, but either can come first.

Living in a Healthy Milieu

Our holistic health program needs to include more than the concerns of what has been called the "me generation," which I think is a wonderful term. Supposedly, all of us in California, both natives and newcomers, were self-preoccupied, interested only in being health and happy. But that *is* the beginning, as I see it. What do you have to give if you are walking around being unhappy and unhealthy? What could you give to a social movement? We have to clean up our own acts first, and then we have to clean up the environment.

We have made a mess of the world we live in. We have inherited tremendous opportunities from past generations, but we have also inherited the mess. We have to start being conscious of what we can do about that, not just by supporting the world wildlife fund, etc., but by what we do in our daily lives, like using low-phosphate detergents, avoiding clothes made of synthetic fibers that don't allow for air circulation, not using products that come from endangered animal species. Walk barefoot periodically, to strengthen your feet and really feel the earth. Avoid smoke-filled rooms and toxic fumes. Avoid noise pollution; get away sometime into the quiet of the mountains and the ocean, just the bliss of the silence and beauty. Turn off lights and appliances when not in use. Drive a car that gets 20 miles per gallon or better. Keep your thermostat below 70 degrees.

How are we going to make all these changes? The power to make them lies within you.

The Holistic Approach to Health

I have a concern that holistic health not become a grab bag of new techniques: try this and try that. A piecemeal approach is not holistic. We have to be sensible about how we use the word holistic. Certainly all modalities of healing, ancient as well as modern, deserve exploration, and should be used where appropriate. We have learned a tremendous amount about the usefulness of acupuncture, laying on of hands, and spiritual healing in the hands of competent individuals. I am concerned that we need an integration between medical science and these newer (or older) techniques. We have had too rigid a boundary to the medical field. Certainly we don't, for example, want to treat a brain tumor with chiropractic, even though there may be other things that chiropractic is extremely useful and important for. Let's not use numerology to treat something that really requires an antibiotic. We need a science of health, not just a science of illness. Again, many people can contribute to that science of health, not just the M.D.

Keep in mind, as you design and develop your own holistic-health program, that it is not a magical transformation. You cannot decide today to make some changes, to design your own holistic-health program, and then expect the following day to turn yourself into a Cinderella or a Prince Charming. Also, keep in mind that the real purpose of health is not just to feel good physically; the real purpose is spiritual growth.

We want to live better, more healthily, and longer not just to enjoy it, but to fulfill the higher purpose for which life was given to us. The healthy body is meant to be a worthy temple in which the spirit can grow and develop. In your essential nature you are divine: that is the major focus of our holistic health movement. We need to perfect and refine our divine spirit. There is evidence now accumulating that we may be eternal, as we have heard from Elisabeth Kubler-Ross and Raymond Mudy. We may be a part of a huge cosmic school; we keep coming back for more and more lessons. At one time that would have seemed the wildest idea imaginable to me, but the evidence seems to be accumulating, and it seems no more plausible to me than the fact that we are here in the first place. Here we are: what a miracle it is! We are all participating every moment in a million miracles that allow us to exist and to celebrate our spirit. We are participating in a supreme intelligence of the highest order.

The Social Context of Holistic Health

Holistic health didn't just grow suddenly on its own. It is part of an idea whose time has come. It is much more than just a reaction against the failure of medicine in the health sector. Holistic health is part of a flow that we have been seeing clearly for the last decade or two, although its roots go much further back. The human potential movement, "Make love not war": these are also parts of this flow.

We here in the West are suffering in many ways from the problems of overconsumption. Our malnutrition and malcontentment result from overconsumption, whereas the other half of the world suffers from malnutrition because there aren't enough resources to go around. Half the people in the world exist on less than $100 per year. I am not saying that we should all wear sack clothes, but couldn't we give up our third automobile, the sailboat, the private plane? If we simplify our lives, we can actually enjoy more. We wind up being healthier and happier because we have fewer hassles. We start having control over things instead of being controlled by them. Having more joyous simplicity doesn't mean that we all have to go back to the land or take up voluntary poverty. But if we think about the larger picture, and about how our own best interests are actually the same as the interests of all people, we will all enjoy higher degrees of spiritual abundance, a fuller and richer inner life.

We are going to see the emergence of more and more holistic values, no matter what we do, because this is a process whose time has come. We should all participate in it, just for the joy and fun of it. Just as the sun is going to rise, the process doesn't need our help; yet we should participate in it just because it is just so neat. We are going to see cooperation become more important than competition. People will strive to develop win-win situations rather than just win-lose ones, to learn internal restraints as opposed to external control, to learn self-expression rather than self-repression, to put evolutionary goals ahead of survival fears.

As we grow in this process, we are going to find that the most important centers for holistic health we build will be the ones within each of us. You have a center for holistic health that has been within you all the time, waiting for you to move in and develop your potential to a maximum. As we each do this, we are going to see develop a network of light and love, health and wholeness, whose social effects will, I hope, be irreversible.

2 PHYSICAL AWARENESS AND HEALING

THE NEW HEALERS FOCUS their work through the systems of the body, the mind, and the spirit. In this section we present five remarkable researchers whose ideas, philosophy, and practice focus on the human body.

The body telegraphs the profound effects of disease and well-being. There are many different techniques and practices that use the body as a focus for healing. Both Eastern and Western practices have been called holistic, in that they bring about mental and spiritual change by working through the body. The four approaches to bodywork described here are only a few of the many used in holistic health. In the hands of these healers the results have been outstanding.

In this section, Dr. Joseph Kamiya speaks of his research that led to the discovery of biofeedback. His work enabled the development of machines that introduced both the holistic health field and allopathic medicine to the idea that the involuntary systems of the body could be trained to respond to voluntary control.

"Movement and the Mind," by Moshe Feldenkrais and Will Shutz, brings together their understanding of the Feldenkrais techniques for reorientation and education of the body and mind. Dr. Feldenkrais, by curing himself of a disabling handicap, developed a new method of schooling human consciousness of the body's motor apparatus. Living in Tel Aviv, he has developed a world-famous practice and teaching schedule.

What is striking about the New Healers is the unique discoveries and adaptations they have made in their fields of practice. Not only are these healers following the basic concepts of holistic health, but they have created new methods and combined old and new practices to pursue the goals of well-being and the creation of wellness.

Dr. Linus Pauling, twice winner of the Nobel Prize, explains the concept that megadoses of Vitamin C may combat viruses, including the common cold virus. Dr. Pauling, an eminent scientist, shares with us a personal view on a controversial subject.

In the last article in this section, Judith McKinnon talks about the development of Intuitive Massage. Ms. McKinnon combined the spiritual with bodywork.

The five researchers and healers in this section give us an unusual opportunity to discover how the body can be the focus for the reeducation toward well-being.

A.P.K.

3 THE DISCOVERY OF BIOFEEDBACK

Joseph Kamiya, Ph.D.

Biofeedback has become a household term. We use the process every day, automatically, within ourselves to regulate the ways our bodies function. Today biofeedback techniques are at the frontier of medical application. They are used for a variety of physical and psychosomatic complaints. Biofeedback practitioners assist people in learning voluntary control of the automatic processes of the mind and body. Most often biofeedback is used to reduce stress, tension headaches, insomnia, pain, and lack of concentration. But its proponents feel they are just beginning to know how best to use the process. There is talk of using it for achieving deep relaxation, as preventive medicine in the control of heart disease, for increasing sexual response, and even for birth control. The use of biofeedback techniques with children in the classroom and in molding learning is just reaching the educational psychologist. And the idea of using these techniques to add to longevity and increase the quality of life among old people is being considered.

Before the 1960s the idea that a person could gain control of an autonomic physiological process was considered impossible. The use of a machine that would reflect brain activity and could in some way change behavior and body processes would have sounded like fantasy. It was through the work of Joseph Kamiya and others that the founding research emerged in the field of biofeedback.

Joseph Kamiya received his Ph.D. in Social Psychology from the University of California at Berkeley before beginning research at the University of Chicago into voluntary control of normally unconscious states. He is currently Professor of Medical Psychology in residence at the Langley Porter Neuropsychiatric Institute of the University of California Medical School in San Francisco, where he is Director of the Psychophysiology of Consciousness Laboratory. Professor Kamiya is a member of the editorial board of the Biofeedback and Self-Regulation Journal, *and also contributed to the editing of the book* Biofeedback and Self-Control.

Professor Kamiya's pioneer work in biofeedback research led to the development of the first "little brainwave machine," which changed our thinking about the mind and the body. In this article, he shares with us his early experience and his very special insight that led to the development of a new area in human understanding of the mind and of how it can affect the body.

BIOFEEDBACK WAS DISCOVERED at the University of Chicago about 1958. I was interested in doing experiments that might illuminate the nature of human consciousness. As a psychologist, the particular angle that I was interested in was "How does man's internal activity, his brain activity, his total body system, relate to human consciousness?" We were involved at the time in the study of sleeping and dreaming, using electro-encephalographic (EEG) methods to detect the occurrence of dreaming. Dreaming seemed to me to be the most important focus for anyone interested in studying consciousness, because obviously dreams did not come from someplace in the immediate environment, but from an internal source.

Quite often, one finds things while looking for something else. In order to study dreams, we have to look at the brain waves of individuals while they are still awake, so that we can tag the moment when they fall asleep. When people are awake, they will often exhibit, from the back of their heads, a regular rhythm known as alpha waves. These waves have a frequency of about ten hertz (cycles per second), and the total train of waves will wax and wane in size and duration several times a minute.

One idea that intrigued us was whether there might be any kind of conscious concomitant of the fluctuations of this brain rhythm. We used discrimination training, a technique drawn from the behavioristic approach, to see if we could train people to discern the ups and downs of this rhythm. We told the subject, who had electrodes attached to his head, that his task would be to guess which of two states of mind he was in. We could tell in the next room which state he was in by our little brainwave machine, which was attached to his electrodes. From time to time we

Sandra Clemente

*Joseph
Kamiya*

would sound a bell, sometimes when he was showing alpha and sometimes when he was not. He would then guess which of the two states he was in, and we would tell him whether his guess was right or wrong. We would then proceed to the next test.

To our delight, we found that our first subject could learn this task quite well. He could say, whenever we rang a bell, whether he was showing alpha rhythms or not. Of course, this led us to ask him, "How are you doing it?" To our interest, he said he didn't know. That led us to a long chain of studies addressed to the question, "What are the conscious concomitants of these brain rhythms, some of which apparently can't even be verbalized?" Although our first was somewhat atypical, it does happen often that an individual can learn to tell one internal physiological state from another, and yet not be able to tell you a single word about how he thinks he's doing it.

We next discovered that, having trained this person to do this kind of discrimination, we had also apparently taught him to control the states of mind that were associated with these brain rhythms. What happened was that one day, being tired of doing the same old discrimination test, we decided to turn the tables around. We said to the subject, "This time we will ring the bell either once or twice, and we would like you to go into the corresponding state." To our amazement, this individual, having been trained to discern the states, and without any further training, could straightaway put himself in alpha and take himself out of alpha.

We began asking more questions: can people be trained to voluntarily control their brain rhythms? What implications would this have for the whole science of consciousness? What is the state of mind that the individual would have to put himself into in order to produce these brain rhythms? Since we obviously haven't been spanked or rewarded as children for having certain brain rhythms, we have no adequate everyday language to describe these rhythms.

Our research shifted to California. We designed an experiment in which subjects heard a tone that went on when their alpha rhythm was larger than a certain size, and went off when it dropped below that level. The subject would hear a rather random coming and going of the tone; it would be on for a second or two, or ten, then off for similar periods of time. There was no way to predict when it would be present or absent. The subjects were told to either increase or decrease the proportion of time that the tone was on.

Of course, when we told a subject he was supposed to control the tone coming into his room, the first thing he said was, "How am I supposed to do it?" And our reply was, "We're not sure. We're not even sure you can learn to do it." We advised them to simply listen to the tone for awhile to see if the comings and goings of the tone were in any way related to anything they could detect internally about their states of mind.

Over a period of time, by trial and error, by putting themselves in different frames of mind, subjects have discovered certain states of mind that generally seem to be associated with the presence of the tone. These states of mind are often described as a "relaxed alertness," a kind of calmness, in which you are not struggling to make the tone come on, or anything else, but where you are simply letting whatever happens, happen. That seems to favor the coming of the tone. When people first start trying to cause the alpha to stay on longer, they succeed only in decreasing it. Everything they try seems to fail. Finally, they come to the conclusion that it is trying itself that is at fault.

I doubt that the brainwave state known as alpha has any particular value in and of itself. I know many people who have learned to increase their alpha activity, and I'm not aware that it has really changed their lifestyle or personalities. There is something to be said, however, for learning different kinds of internal skills by the use of biofeedback. For example, you can learn how to relax your musculature; by using electrodes attached to the skin which pick up the electrical activity of muscle, you can learn to relax your muscles much more thoroughly than is possible with ordinary voluntary relaxation. You can learn to control heart activity, the temperature of various body parts, such as hands and feet, gastric activity, possibly even acid production.

It has now been reasonably well established that many of these skills can help alleviate some psychosomatic symptoms. For example, learning how to relax the forehead muscles and the entire head-neck region is very useful for people who are suffering from chronic tension headache. Learning how to warm the hands has, for some reason, helped people avoid getting migraine headaches.

The biofeedback machine does not itself stimulate any kind of brainwave or muscle activity. It is a sensing device, very much like a clinical thermometer, the bathroom scales, or simply a mirror. It is, in a real sense, a kind of physiological mirror. It simply shows what is happening inside your body. You can choose to ignore the information, or choose to use it to attempt to gain control of the physiological state.

4 MOVEMENT AND THE MIND
Moshe Feldenkrais, Ph.D.
and Will Schutz, Ph.D.

Dr. Moshe Feldenkrais and Will Schutz, both pioneers in the body and mind movements of the 1960s, bring together in this article their insights and personal experiences. Their work with people emphasizes a reorientation to the environment and a move toward self-consciousness. "Understanding while doing, doing while understanding. . . " They are primary proponents of the concept that the body and mind are integrated, that the mind is experiencing everything that is happening in the body, and that the body is experiencing everything that is happening in the mind. Their philosophy does not accept the dualism of body and mind established in Western medicine; they have found that the body's problems cannot be solved strictly through the body, nor the mind's problems strictly through the mind, as if in isolation.

Both Feldenkrais and Schutz carry on a practice, in which they also train others, of reeducating the body/mind in a self-directed method of change that is experienced in the mind and body and spirit, a guru-less body/mind therapy.

Will Schutz's classroom experiences in teaching psychology at Harvard University (from which he earned his Ph.D.) and the University of Chicago shifted his interest from the strict scientific approach to a personal fascination with small-group dynamics. After teaching at the University of California at Berkeley, he found his way to Esalen, where he studied with many of the pioneers of the human potential movement. He is presently offering courses in a master's degree program in holistic studies at Antioch West. He is the author of many books, of which the most recent is Profound Simplicity.

Moshe Feldenkrais was born in Poland and emigrated as a young man to Palestine. He studied afterwards in France, where he took his doctorate in physics and became an associate of Joliot-Curie. He was an outstanding judoka *(black belt) and soccer player; indeed, soccer decided his fate, in the form of a knee injury he sustained while playing.*

In 1940, while working in Britain on antisubmarine warfare, he consulted a surgeon who told him that an operation on the knee should have been performed years earlier and would now have only a 50-50 chance of success. The odds were not good enough for Feldenkrais, who resolved to teach himself to walk anew. Steeping himself in the literature of anatomy, physiology, psychology, and anthropology and perceiving what the books failed to teach, he developed his own method of schooling the human consciousness of the body's motor apparatus.

Returning to Israel after the war, he decided to give up the paramilitary assignments in which his scientific expertise had continued to involve him and to devote himself to teaching the new technique. Today, he maintains a full program of individual and group teaching, and also lectures at Tel Aviv University. He is the author of Body and Mature Behavior, *and* Awareness through Movement.

Moshe Feldenkrais: Life is movement. If we act, if we move, we exist. If we don't move, we are dead. Therefore, a body that doesn't move is not a living thing. However, a living *body* cannot move by itself. In fact, if we made up a body with the best skeleton available and the finest muscles we could find, and we put them together, we would see that a dumb thing like that wouldn't be able to stand on its feet for a millionth of a second. It would fall because it had no brain. So the brain and the mind are just as much a part of our material structure as the bones and muscles.

Now, the functioning of the brain is quite different from the functioning of the skeleton and the other parts of the material structure. Structure and function must go together in any living thing. The most important aspect of functioning is what the mind does, what the brain does. Who has ever seen a mind without a

courtesy of *New Realities*, Bill Callison

*Moshe
Feldenkrais*

brain? The brain is the material support of the mind, just as the body is the material support of the brain.

Suppose we make a machine that incorporates a skeleton, muscles, organs, and also a brain. Would a brain like that speak English or Turkish? It wouldn't know how to speak at all. Would a brain like that be able to read, to think mathematics, to listen to or create music? Could it make an IBM machine or a microphone? Of course not. When the brain comes into the world, it is fit to do only what any animal brain can do: it attends to breathing, to digestion, to the automatic processes of the body. Beyond that, we must "wire in" that brain to relate to the environment into which it comes. At the outset, the brain doesn't even know how to stand. It cannot read or whistle, or tap dance, or skate, or swim. The brain must be adjusted and connected in order to fully function.

Assume I'm looking at a microphone. When my eyes look at it, I identify the image. Actually, there is no image of a microphone in my brain. There is an image of the microphone on my retina. However, from the retina, the image from each eye is separated into two parts and projected on four different parts of the cerebral cortex, which actually has no real image of a microphone. However, the function of seeing evokes in my mind the thing that I see with my eyes. The brain goes through a type of schooling that "wires" it into objective reality. Reality, therefore, encompasses the environment and the body itself.

For instance, a baby cannot interlace the fingers until the first year has passed. Each child born must explore and learn his or her own body. The mind gradually develops and begins to program the functioning of the brain. My way of looking at the mind and body involves a subtle method of "rewiring" the structure of the entire human being to be functionally well-integrated, which means being able to do what the individual wants. Each individual has the choice to wire the body in a special way. However, the way we do it now is almost completely futile, making everyone aliented from their own capacity to have feelings.

The most important thing is not that we learn, but how we learn. After we are born, what language do we begin to speak? Naturally, it is the language that is spoken where we are born. Therefore, we're wired in by that accident of birth, not by our choice, not by our capacities, not by our talents. Each language embodies cultural traditions and attitudes from thousands of years of development. Consequently, that language wires into us a lot of notions which we don't want, which we accept merely because of learning the language. We learn a lot of old nonsense which perpetuates itself. Obviously, then, when we do learn, we can learn things wrongly.

Each person is born as a humanoid, a human animal. The newborn baby can swallow, suck, digest, excrete, and maintain body temperature like any other animal. What makes us different from animals is that humanoids can develop into *homo sapiens,* human beings with intelligence, knowledge, and awareness.

Will Schutz: Your method is what I would call a self-oriented method, as opposed to a guru-oriented method. When I was doing some of your lessons, one particular example stood out. The problem was how to put my feet apart so that they were most comfortable. You told me to put them very close together and feel what that felt like, then put them very far apart and see what that felt like, and keep moving them back and forth until it felt right. Whatever felt right, was right, was correct. At that same time I was also going through Arica training, which I consider a guru-oriented approach. Oscar Ichazo is the guru, and followers do what he says. I was doing a similar movement there, but the rule there was that you put your feet one forearm-length apart. If you didn't do that, then the instructor would come along and say, "That's not right. You didn't get it correct." What was "right" there depended on remembering what I was told to do by the instructor, rather than on what felt right to me.

Moshe Feldenkrais: I never force anyone to accept my view. I would never say "this is correct" or "this is incorrect." To me there is nothing correct. However, if you do something, and don't know what you are doing, it's incorrect, for you. If you do know what you are doing, then whatever you do, you are correct. As human beings we have the peculiar ability, which other animals do not have, to know what we are doing. That's why we have freedom of choice.

Suppose I see you placing your feet apart at a distance which I consider incorrect. Now, why do I consider it incorrect? Not because I think it should be a certain length, but because I feel that you are really uncomfortable, and are standing that way only because you have never actually visualized what distance is necessary in order to feel comfortable. You're not really concerned with whether it's comfortable or not. If you're very shy or if you are a virginal girl, you hold your feet together because it's prescribed to be "decent." If you are a show-off extrovert, wanting to show how important and free you are, you will open your legs much too wide. Much too wide for whom? Not for me. I don't say "this is right" and "this is wrong." I say that if you *know* that you are holding your feet close because you are shy, and you feel awkward spreading them more, there is no harm. From my point of view, it's correct; do what you like. I am not here to tell you what to do. I am here only to show you that you should do what you know you are doing. However, if you don't really *know* that you hold your feet like that, and you believe that all human beings should hold their feet together, and you are virtually unable to open them, not because your physiology or your anatomy doesn't permit it, but because you are so unaware that you don't know that they can be opened, then it's incorrect.

Will Schutz: I remember an example in one of the lessons I took with you, where that was illustrated. We were following some instructions, and one person in the class would not do it the way you said. Rather than bawl him out, you asked the rest of the class to do it the way he did it, then do it the way you said to do it, and to judge for ourselves which way was more comfortable. The process helped us to increase our awareness of what actually felt better.

Moshe Feldenkrais: There's more to it than that. My point was that I said something, and the great majority of people did it in one way. There was one who somehow interpreted the same words quite differently. Now, it's possible that he is an idiot, that he can't understand what I'm talking about. That's all right. However, I believe that he isn't an idiot, that instead he's so far away from being able to function as I asked that he can't conceive that I meant what I said.

Now, all the other people did it as asked. I tell all of them, "Look, look how this person does it. Maybe he is right; perhaps it should be done like that. Can you imitate him?" Yes, everybody can. "Can you do it the way you did before?" Yes, they all can, but he can only do it in his way; he cannot do it like all the others. Hence they have the freedom of choice between two acts, but he is a compulsive, unable to change. He doesn't know what he is doing; he can't do what he wants.

That technique, making you look at him, makes it easy for him to look at himself. I can say to him, "Look, you have done it as you have. Maybe you are right. These people can do like you, or can do something else, but you have no choice. You are a computer; they are human beings. They have free will; they have choice. You haven't. Now, sit and look. Can you see?" By seeing the others imitating him, he suddenly realizes that he didn't know what he was doing. As soon as he realizes that, he does it exactly like all the others. His learning takes ten seconds. He recaptures his freedom of choice and regains human dignity.

Understand that there are two sorts of learning. There is the kind of learning which is committing things to memory; for instance, taking a telephone book and learning it by heart, or taking an anatomy book and learning the attachments and origins of each muscle. That learning is independent of time and experience. You can decide to do it at any time. But suppose you want to play the piano. Every time you begin to learn, you say, "Look, all right, I haven't played the piano as a child. Now it's so difficult to start it, and what's the point of playing the piano? I am a scientist; I am a radio interviewer. What do I have to play the piano for? If I need a piano, somebody plays the piano on records." But for some people, like Yehudi Menuhin or Vladimir Horowitz, the making of music is more important than your radio or your science. They learn by a type of learning which is almost beyond personal choice. You can learn the phone book if you want to, or not learn it if you don't want to; and you can change your mind.

But there is a learning in which you have no say whatsoever, and that learning is latent in the natural laws which have produced our brain and our nervous system and our body and our muscles. These laws are included in the cosmic laws of the universe. They are so precise and so sequential that you have no say about the order you will learn them in. They must be learned in that order; if not, you will not develop as a normal human being. You will be a cripple or an autistic child—something not normal. Why can't you teach a baby even a year old to hold a pencil and write? The baby cannot write until the capacity develops.

You see, there is a kind of learning which goes with growth. You cannot skate before you can walk, no matter how clever you are, even if you are a genius. You must first learn to walk. You cannot walk before you crawl. If you learn to walk before you crawl, you will be a cripple. You cannot learn to speak before you are vertical. You know why you can't? In the human nervous system, each part comes into function in a sequence, one after another. The functioning helps the growth at each stage as a new part of this brain comes into dominance, and changes the entire way of action. This type of learning must proceed at its own pace. We have no say in it. However, because this learning is done under human direction, it may be done in a different way than was intended by nature.

My way of learning, my way of dealing with people, is to find out, for that person who wants it, what sort of accomplishment is possible for that person. People can learn to move and walk and stand differently, but they have given up because they think it's too late now, that the growth process has been completed, that they can't learn something new, that they don't have the time or ability. You don't have to go back to being a baby in order to function properly. You can, at any time of your life, rewire yourself, provided I can convince you that there is nothing permanent or compulsive in your system, except what you believe to be so.

I don't treat patients. I give lessons to help a person learn about himself or herself. Learning comes by the experience of the manipulation. I don't treat people, I don't cure people, and I don't teach people. I tell them stories, because I believe that learning is the most important thing for a human being. Learning should be a pleasant, marvelous experience. Very often in the lesson, I say, "Look, would you stop? So many of you look so stern, as if you were trying to do something terrible, difficult, and unpleasant for you. That means you're tired, you won't understand any more. Break it, go and have a coffee, and stop it. Or let me tell you a story so that I can see the brightness in your eyes and a smile on your face, and that you'll listen and find that what I say is important to you."

Will Schutz: To me, that is very important, but it isn't the main thing you do. You do talk, and you do make these points, but the big thing is what goes on with the hands. To watch a Feldenkrais lesson for me is a meditation. It's very quiet and sensitive, and it's in the hands where the things happen. There's a communication from the body to the brain that's going on without any words, through the hands. The talk usually comes later.

5 VITAMINS AND ORTHOMOLECULAR MEDICINE

Linus Pauling, Ph.D.

Use of megadoses of Vitamin C merely to alleviate and prevent colds is a controversial subject in orthomolecular medicine. The use of Vitamin C to combat viral disease in general is a challenging concept.

Dr. Pauling is a prime advocate of the use of Vitamin C. As a chemist he has contributed greatly to the understanding of molecular structures, particularly with regard to chemical bonding. He is the only person who has received two unshared Nobel Prizes, one for Chemistry in 1954, and the Peace Prize in 1962. He was educated at the California Institute of Technology, Pasadena, and in Europe.

He is the author of many articles and books. Those dealing with his theories on megadoses of Vitamin C and bonding are Vitamin C, the Common Cold, and the Flu, *and* Vitamin C and the Common Cold. *He coauthored* Orthomolecular Psychiatry: Treatment of Schizophrenia *with David Hawkins.*

His lifelong contributions to science and mankind are too numerous to list in this brief introduction to his work. He is held in the highest esteem by his colleagues and is seen as a model for younger scientists.

Now 78, and a Professor Emeritus at Stanford University, he is actively doing research on the effects of nutrition on the rate of malignant tumor growth at the Linus Pauling Institute of Science and Medicine. His major interest is the analysis of body fluids, blood, and urine to help in the diagnosis of diseases.

It was the same research on the structure and forces of molecules which won him the Nobel Prize in 1954 and that has culminated in his famous "orthomolecular" approach to the maintenance of health.

*The word means "correct or right molecules" and expresses his con-
cept that consumption of appropriate types and amounts of nutritional elements, especially vitamins, is needed for optimum health in
the individual. Professor Pauling believes that the work on cancer
and Vitamin C may well turn out to be the most important job in
which the institute is involved.*

I ACQUIRED MY DEEP INTEREST in vitamin research in 1954,
when the principal man working on the hereditary hemolytic
anemias was assigned to my laboratory in Pasadena. I didn't really want to try to compete with him (I thought I would come out
second-best, anyway), and thought I had better try something
else. I said to myself: "I'll look for another field. It ought to be an
important one. If I am going to try to find other molecular
diseases, they might as well be important diseases."

The important diseases are, it seems to me, mental illness
and cancer, which both cause a great amount of suffering. At that
time, almost everybody was working on cancer, almost no one on
mental illness; so I thought I had better work on mental illness,
which I did for ten years, until I left the California Institute of
Technology.

In this work, my associates and I mostly studied the conditions, some of them genetic, that cause mental retardation. We
also did some work on schizophrenia. While we were working on
schizophrenia, I learned about two men working in Canada,
Abraham Hoffer and Humphrey Osmond, who in 1952 had
observed that some patients with schizophrenia improved greatly
when they were given tremendously large doses of niacin or
niacinamide, two forms of the pellagra-preventing factor (now
classed as B vitamins) that had been discovered back in 1937.
Their schizophrenic patients were given doses of 17 grams a day.
The amount recommended by the Food and Nutrition Board (the
RDA or recommended dietary allowance) is 17 mg a day; that is,
they were giving these patients a thousand times the recommended amount of this vitamin. They and other investigators later
found that similarly large doses of Vitamin C were also very
beneficial to patients with schizophrenia and other mental illnesses.

*Linus
Pauling*

I was puzzled by these findings. It hadn't occurred to me—although it had to other people—that the vitamins, which are organic compounds required in very small amounts for life and good health, had any other function than preventing the corresponding deficiency disease. That is, you get scurvy and die if you don't get any Vitamin C; you get pellagra and die if you don't get any Vitamin B3, or niacin or niacinamide.

Vitamin C was discovered by Albert Szent-Gyorgyi in the late 1920s. He had said in 1937 that there are tremendous possibilities for improving the health of people by use of vitamins if they were given in the amounts that lead to the best health; yet his recommendation had been pretty much ignored.

I had continued taking about a gram a day of Vitamin C ever since 1937; the current RDA is only 45 mg, a little less than a twentieth of a gram. As I thought about this problem, I also read the literature, and I found many papers on the benefits to people that result from having them take very large amounts of one vitamin or another. I began asking myself, what happens to the human body when these larger amounts are ingested? Can we really prevent and treat disease by using these substances, which are normally present in the human body?

I thought this work, which Hoffer and Osmond and other people had been doing, to be so important that it ought to have a name. I invented the term orthomolecular medicine in 1967. Orthomolecular means "right molecules," taken in the right amounts. The right molecules are those that are normally present in the humn body, and the right amounts are the amounts that put you in the best of health. But here we have a problem. What are the right amounts of these substances? This problem has been ignored. Even though Szent-Gyorgyi had talked about it back in 1937, nobody had done anything significant about it.

Solving this problem, discovering the "right amounts," is made more difficult by the biochemical individuality of human beings. The amount that puts me in the best health might not be the amount that puts you in the best health. It is also quite hard to measure a person's state of health. For example, I testified before the Federal Trade Commission in a suit involving the Coca-Cola Company, which had put out advertising claiming that each glass of its High C is the equivalent of a glass of orange juice. In fact, a glass of orange juice contains 90 mg of ascorbic acid, a glass of High C only 45 or 50 mg; but it was ruled that, since nobody needs more than 45 mg, it was all right to say that 45 mg is equal to 90 mg. However, we do have some evidence about the amount of Vitamin C that leads to good health. I argued then, and I continue to argue, that you can use the incidence of disease as a measure of the state of your health. If you catch colds that last a long time, if you come down with the flu often, if you have aches and pains, arthritis, prostatitis, or other troubles (of course, these troubles affect older people more than younger people), then you have a measure of the state of your health; and you can check to see whether increasing the intake of Vitamin C decreases the manifestations of the disease.

The minimum daily requirements were established by studies on the deficiency diseases. The Food and Nutrition Board would take people, volunteers in good health, and put them on a diet that contained no Vitamin C. After three or four months, the subjects would come down with scurvy. Then they were given enough Vitamin C to cause the obvious symptoms of scurvy to go away. It was found that about 10 mg a day usually sufficed. Of course, these experiments are hard to do. You will naturally have trouble getting volunteers who will submit to such experiments, and the Board didn't have very many, perhaps ten or twenty. Then you need to ask how many people there are in the United States, say, who are different enough from these volunteers that 10 mg a day wouldn't keep them from getting scurvy. To be on the safe side, the British decided to recommend 20 mg a day. In the United States the recommended amount was 75 mg a day; it was later reduced to 60 mg a day, then a few years ago it was reduced to 45 mg a day. It's hard to understand why these changes have been made. I am sure these numbers don't have much significance, except for keeping people from dying of scurvy. They don't have any significance in terms of how much you need to be in really good health.

With Vitamin C, all the B vitamins and most of the other vitamins, warnings about overdoses are virtually groundless. People have eaten as much as half a pound of Vitamin C in a day without any manifestations of toxicity. No one knows what the lethal dose might be. Vitamin C is one of the least toxic substances known. You can eat far more Vitamin C than you can eat salt, for example. I don't think it's nearly as harmful to people as ordinary sugar is.

One of the first properties of Vitamin C that was discovered is that it is required for the synthesis of collagen. Collagen is the principle constituent of connective tissue. It holds the body together. It is a constituent of tendons, of skin, of fibrils, giving them strength, and of the protein in bone. It also strengthens the intercellular cement that holds the cells together in all the organs and body. Accordingly, if we have the right intake of Vitamin C, which is quite a large intake, we manufacture enough of this connective tissue to give our bodies strength.

Death by scurvy consists of the body's falling apart. The joints fall apart; the blood vessels fall apart, so that you get internal bleeding. The functioning of the body ultimately ceases. If we want to have our tissues strong, to resist foreign invaders, which can be viruses or bacteria, or malignant tumors growing and infiltrating the normal tissues, we need to produce the right amount of collagen. The evidence is that a good intake of ascorbic acid does this job.

The various natural protective mechanisms of the body, for example, the lymphocytes or white cells, which are the soldiers of the body that attack invaders and destroy them, can eat up bacteria or other cells that are recognized as foreign, such as malignant cells. The cell of a cancer growth in the human body is, of course, derived from one of the normal cells of the body by a process of change. This process of change identifies it as a foreign cell, so that the lymphocytes can attack it and destroy it, which they do in many cancer patients in whom the cancers regress, or who have circulating malignant cells that then disappear from the body, so that the patient regains good health and continues to live.

A couple of years ago, it was shown by investigators at the National Cancer Institute that people who ingest 5 grams of Vitamin C a day produce twice as many new lymphocytes by the process of lymphocyte blastogenesis as those who ingest the ordinary small amounts. If they ingest 10 grams a day, they produce perhaps three times as many, or perhaps even more. No one knows how this process continues with larger amounts. There is no doubt that one of the ways in which Vitamin C helps protect the body against cancer and all kinds of infectious diseases is by stimulating the lymphocytes to increase blastogenesis.

We also know that Vitamin C has a direct inactivating effect on the viruses that produce the common cold and such diseases as infectious hepatitis, measles, or influenza. How important this effect of Vitamin C is, as compared with the stimulation of the body's natural protective mechanism, hasn't yet been discovered.

In general, physicians don't like the idea of people treating themselves or prescribing for themselves. This, of course, is what is done largely with vitamins. In fact, of course, many physicians do prescribe vitamins, and they tend to prescribe the high-priced ones, which are no better than the cheap ones. Forty years ago, when the vitamins first became available, there was a lot of enthusiasm among the medical people for vitamins. For the most part, they didn't use them in the amounts in which they are used now, but a few physicians did try one gram or even two grams of Vitamin C a day on cancer patients and on patients with other diseases. Then the sulfa drugs and the antibiotics were discovered in the period 1935 to 1945. These drugs are so effective against infectious diseases that most medical people lost interest in the vitamins. There were a few physicians, Dr. McCormack in Canada, who is dead now, and Dr. Fred Kliner in Reedsville, N.C., who continued to work with vitamins and who wrote papers giving the results of their observations on patients and contending that Vitamin C and other vitamins have a big effect in controlling disease. But these papers were almost entirely ignored.

The National Cancer Institute alone spends over $800 million a year on cancer research. Of this, perhaps a few hundred thousand dollars all together, I would estimate, goes into the study of the effect of Vitamin C on cancer. It is hard for me to understand the lethargy of the oncologists, their outright antagonism to the idea that such a simple substance as Vitamin C can have value. I know of this because of the letters that I get from them. I feel that medical men, physicians, surgeons, should be conservative, that they shouldn't gallop off in all directions on their hobby horses, and shift from one remedy to another as the wind shifts. But, I am astonished that the people at the National Cancer Institute, for example, and in the American Cancer Society have such closed minds to the possibility that something new has come along.

I wrote to the National Cancer Advisory Board and the Director of the National Cancer Institute, saying that, from my study of what is going on in cancer research, the National Cancer Institute is quite unable, apparently, to assess the value of a new idea, or even to recognize that an idea has value.

I would say that NCI, in its own work and in the grants that it makes, is very good at development. The NCI spends hundreds of millions of dollars supporting studies in which one anticancer drug is compared with another in a couple of hundred cancer patients who are given one drug or a mixture of three drugs or five drugs. You can go on for an infinite length of time, bringing in variations on this same theme, and they do that very well.

6 INTUITIVE MASSAGE
Judith McKinnon

Touch is life-giving; without it infants and children die. Humans need touch; it is the oldest method of healing. In recent years, touch through massage has come to be a recognized part of health practice. There are many methods of massage, various methods being practiced all over the world. All have release of tension as a common goal. Another type of massage that is growing popular is the holistic massage, which combines traditional massage techniques with fantasy and inner healing.

Judith McKinnon is both a practitioner and a teacher of holistic massage. Her work during the past years has become increasingly more important in the holistic movement. In this article Ms. McKinnon shares with us the evolution of this process, which provides relaxation, growth, and self-learning for the subject of the healing experience.

LEARNING TO BE sensitive to body blocks was a very slow awakening for me. When I moved to California, people were talking about all kinds of things I had never heard of. I began to take classes, in massage, bio-energetics, sensory awareness, and meditation. As I immersed myself in them, I began to know things that I could not account for, and I began to think that I was crazy because I knew them. For example, I knew my mother's address a month before she moved, and since she had lived in the same house for 30 years, it wasn't likely that she would be moving at all. I began tapping into an energy source, but I became very frightened by it, and tried to squelch it. I was very fortunate to have a psychiatrist who did not put down these abilities, but helped me to understand them and to come to value them. It still took many years before I began to really use and appreciate what I had. Now I feel quite comfortable.

Like other practitioners in the so-called "holistic health" field, I have experienced difficulty in finding a precise label for what I do. I have tried calling my work "psychic massage," but discovered I didn't really feel comfortable with that term. I then tried "energy massage," but since I also use direct body contact in my work, that didn't seem appropriate either. Finally, I settled on "intuitive massage" as a way of describing my approach.

"Intuitive massage" does not mean the abandonment of traditional body-massage techniques. It does not mean that the practitioner is ungrounded. It simply means that after learning techniques, after understanding the body's physiology and anatomy, the practitioner must let go of concepts and preconceptions, and become free to move from an inner space in relation to the client.

In my classes, I try to teach my students how to tune into their own intuitive natures. I begin by having them feel the energy in their own hands, working with imagery, and breathing. I direct them to feel the energy fields around the body: how, for example, on the left side it might be rather small, and on the right side quite large; how a person might have a lot of energy around the top of the head and very little as you feel down to the feet. Then I try to teach them, using a combination of energy and traditional body-massage techniques, to release the blocked energies and to balance the imbalances.

What needs to be recognized is that tension comes from the pain in people's lives. We don't get tense from a day of pleasure at the beach with a friend. We get tense from the experiences that affect us adversely. So whenever we are dealing with a person's tension in massage, we must realize that we are dealing with pain, with life pain, both physically and emotionally.

Moreover, these tensions can be very old. It is important to realize that the attitudes which they reflect and reinforce once served us well, in the past, but since then they have become inappropriate.

Very often we grow, but we don't realize we've grown. I try to get people to see that blockages which appear to be problems

Sandra Clemente

Judith
McKinnon

now, may once have been necessary armor against the slings and arrows of some circumstance. I don't need to be angry that my shoulders are tight, for example. What I need is to see that this tightness no longer serves my development and growth.

I begin work with a client, by channeling energy. I draw energy through the top of my head, i.e., through my crown chakra, and send it out through my hands. I focus the energy on a blocked area, and work with it to open the area and release the flow. At the same time, I tap into the person's ability to work with himself. For example, I will give him a visualization. If a shoulder is the problem, I may have him visualize one shoulder as lighter and the shoulder that is troubling him as darker. I will have him breathe light into the dark shoulder, drawing it down through the crown and into the troubled area. Or, if I am working with someone who can't cope with "breathing light," I may have her visualize a stick of butter being taken from the freezer and put on the table. Then I will have her visualize it thawing, and then being moved near the stove, where it begins to melt, as the tension in her body begins to release. The visualizations I use are always different, because they are geared to the specific person I am working on, as are all my techniques.

In my classes, I teach each student to create his or her own massage. Each body you work on is going to be different. Each massage practitioner is going to bring something different to the massage. His or her hands, physical strength, energy, and perception will all be different.

If a person has for years had people look down on his physical body, and has never had it appreciated, he will probably not appreciate it himself. He will be disconnected from his body, and will withdraw energy from his body and into his head. In this society, we really cherish our heads, our thought processes. All our energy is drawn into our heads, and we keep getting bigger heads. Sometimes I feel the energy around a person's head, and it extends out eight to ten inches. It is literally a big head. It takes up a lot of space. Then I feel his or her body, and there is nothing happening, no movement, no energy. The only way to connect with such a person is verbally. If you ask him what he is feeling, he doesn't know. He is disconnected. The way I work with such a person is to slowly draw the energy from the head back into the body, and to verbalize what I see.

If you massage an area of the body from which a person is disconnected, he will tend not to feel it. If you massage the legs, calves, or feet of a person who is ungrounded, for example, he will not get much from it. But if you massage his neck, where all the energy is bottled up, it will feel fantastic to him.

It is very exciting to see people reclaim their bodies. Our body is our home, for now. It is what we get our sense of security from. How we fit into our bodies, how we are able to take up space in the world, determines whether we feel we deserve this space or whether we are apologetic about existing at all. Everyone knows people who bend and curl their bodies, who cannot allow themselves to just sit in the room and be there. They draw their energy down to where they don't feel they are taking up too much space.

It is sad that many people don't feel able to assert their natural-born right simply to be, to feel good about being in the world. The right was stolen from them, in a sense. When there is a lot of tension in a person's hips and legs, it will affect his grounding, his sense of security. He will feel as if he has no ground to stand on, and will be unable to assert himself. If you loosen up his legs and hips, so that the energy can move down and through the feet, you put him in touch with the ground, and he will be able to stand up for himself.

Often people come to me with contractions in their body that have resulted from basic negative situations in their lives. There is no way I can get rid of the contractions in a single massage session. It would take weeks, sometimes years, to undo them. If a muscle problem results from a present problem, then, even if it is deep, short-term work can undo it. But if it is a very old contraction, therapy may be needed to deal with the attitudes and situations that have created it. I often work in conjunction with therapists. Clients come to me because as their attitudes change and their minds get into a different space, they begin to feel bogged down by their bodies. They are being held back. Working with the body contributes to the healing process; it is part of the process.

No one is going to get massaged every day; but they are certainly going to accumulate tension every day. So people have to learn to take care of themselves. One thing I run up against in teaching people to take care of themselves is that they really don't want to. They resent taking care of themselves because they want someone to take care of them. From all my years of working with people, I have come to the conclusion that no one has gotten enough nourishment in early life. That is one way of summing up what massage is about. It is a delayed nourishment. But just as we can't regress to a childhood state and be taken care of by a parent all the time, so the massage practitioner has a responsibility to help the subject to help himself. That means not only to heal, but to teach the arts of self-healing; not only to nourish, but to teach the secrets of self-nourishment.

3 MENTAL AWARENESS AND HEALING

A MAJORITY OF THE NEW HEALERS have had personal experiences of overcoming illness in extraordinary ways. Throughout this book, there are stories of men and women whose health was changed by some transforming experience outside the traditional forms of modern medicine.

The mind is a powerful part of the body/mind/spirit triad of self. It has become the new frontier of learning since the 1960s. Although we have some basic information about the working of the brain and its physiology, men and women with uncommon curiosity and creativity are exploring the phenomena of the mind and their relationships to biofeedback, stress and healing, inner control of pain, meditation, hypnosis, and sexuality. It is not without good reason that the brain has been called the most important sex organ.

It would be easy for the New Healers to fall into thinking that all health is in the mind, but the research and practices founded on mental awareness see it as a tool for healing and for maintaining high-level wellness. Holistic health principles advocate the use of positive thinking, holding thoughts of wellness, using self-healing fantasies to promote well-being.

Practitioners who use the mind as the focus of healing do so in a variety of ways. Many of the therapies used in the personal growth movement of the mid-1960s to 1970s can be adapted to holistic health concepts. To allow inner healing to take place one must have a positive attitude, and come to terms with life problems.

In this section, Dr. James "Josh" Carter shares with us his experience of being healed by meditation. He gives us his insights as a scientist and researcher in the field of health and alternative healings.

"Self-Healing and Voluntary Control of the Body," by Jack Schwarz, presents a view, from personal insight, that pain can be voluntarily controled. To gain this mastery, Mr. Schwarz's techniques involve the use of meditation, self acceptance, and joy of living.

Dr. Irving Oyle, writer, lecturer, and former Director of the Bolinas Headlands Clinic, discusses in his article the concept that the mind/body are united and that all healing is self-healing. Attitudes about health and disease can be changed and directed toward improvement of health by the use of western medicine and holistic practices.

"Overcoming Dualism," by Patricia Sun, addresses the issue of integrating body/mind/spirit. Ms. Sun explains her healing practice with the use of sound and energy through the power of love.

A.P.K.

7 DISEASE AND CONFLICT
James T. Carter, O.D.

Dr. "Josh" Carter is a natural-health practitioner, optometrist, and research scientist. His practice unifies Chinese medical philosophies with Western biological sciences. His work has helped to initiate and clarify new health policies, and to provide for the integration of public-health strategies and emerging health practices.

Dr. Carter studied at the University of California School of Optometry, and is well-known for his work and research in the field of iridology. Iridology is the science of diagnosing physical illness and imbalance from the marks and color changes in the iris of the human eye. In this article, "Disease and Conflict" Dr. Carter talks about his personal experience in being healed, and how he came to see most disease as resulting from a conflict in consciousness that is not handled appropriately. If it is allowed to progress, the conflict becomes more gross, and disease results. Obviously when one is dis-eased, one is out of harmony with nature and with self. Disease as conflict is a very old idea in the approach to health. Primitive people, tribal people, American Indians, see illness as a form of being out of harmony with nature, since the mind and body and nature are intertwined. By reviving this old concept of man and nature, Dr. Carter has advanced the return of Western medicine to holism.

HOLISTIC HEALTH INVOLVES LOOKING at more than just the physical organs and systems in isolation. Holistic health encompasses the emotional, social, and other aspects of our being as well.

Most disease as we know it is a conflict: a crisis in consciousness that results in a crisis in body. We may see a malfunc-

Christopher Wentworth

Josh Carter (left) and Richard Miles (right)

tion in a certain area of the body; and we may see an emotional crisis or conflict; but there are other levels we can't normally see when we first look at the workings of our own bodies. We might test the blood, to get a reading on a glucose tolerance test, for example, but that doesn't tell us anything about a conflict in consciousness.

I see conflict as a movement of awareness from a subtle to a gross stage. It starts out with an imperceptible change, a conflict that usually slips by our waking consciousness, a choice that takes place in one of the more subtle bodies, such as the mental body or the emotional body. As one experiences this upset but doesn't handle it, the conflict gets progressively more and more gross, and disease results. Morbidity is a direct function of unconsciousness. Obviously the grossest from of disease is death, when the conflict is so overwhelming that one cannot survive it.

Usually this progression takes place in characteristic stages. Initially there are mental imbalances, of attitudes, thoughts, ideas, belief structures, mental constructs, which create patterns of conflict within consciousness. Usually these conflicts can be resolved with a little clarity, a little wisdom. Sometimes it's sufficient to simply throw it all out as being "normal" craziness.

Often the conflict is not resolved, and we progress to a more gross level, usually involving a relationship to another person. The patterns of behavior in the emotional body are becoming affected, as these mental attitudes begin to have emotional counterparts. We start feeling resentment; maybe we experience a little fear, a little doubt, certain kinds of depression. Now we are manifesting something that we can see and other people can also see, and they may give feedback. Sometimes this emotional conflict can be thrown off also. This crisis can sometimes "come to a head," and be clarified on the emotional level. The process of clarification generally involves communication with another person.

If a person begins to experience physical pain, the progression has obviously gone to an even more gross level. The organ systems are saying, "Because of this conflict, we're going to have to turn this organ up and turn this one down. Let's increase secretions of this organ about twofold, and maybe this person will recognize that a problem exists."

By this time we can view disease as a message. The component parts of the body are saying, "We have a need here, an unmet need." The whole healing process begins with handling unmet needs. In our professional schools, as doctors, we're all taught that the key purpose of our profession is to take care of unmet needs. We've gotten very far away from seeing clearly what a need really is, and what it takes to fulfill a need. We're usually into replacing organ systems or functions; if that gland isn't working well, let's just make it look like it works by putting in insulin. Or let's make it appear that there's no problem by removing the gland, and saying that the body can still make it because it seems all right. The person who is usually in tremendous amounts of pain is going through a more serious conflict, and is calling for much more help than would be needed on just the mental and emotional level. The call needs to be met by resources, by compassion, sometimes by gross physical intervention.

However, let us not pass by this opportunity for responsible personal transformation, for understanding disease as a positive experience. We need to understand that disease is not something we "get," but something we *do.*

I had a dramatic personal experience during my last year at

the University of California. There I was, about to graduate with my Doctor of Optometry degree, having been trained to understand the nature of the disease process from the academic point of view. Looking back on it, I realize I didn't understand the nature of disease, because somehow I contracted a pretty serious case of hepatitis. When my mother found out, she contacted a healer in London named George Chapman, who arranged a meditation involving himself in England, and myself in Berkeley. I had no preconceived notions about this meditation. Indeed, I could only muster about half an hour of energy during the day where I could actually sit up and take a little food like molasses and milk. My skin had turned yellow; I was tremendously jaundiced.

Anyway, I sat up in bed that night at ten o'clock and just passively said, okay, whatever happens, will happen. I had no direction, except just to begin to meditate. Suddenly, a whole process of conscious visualization began to come through me. I saw the whole origin of my condition and the things that I needed to do to change it. The visualization went through various phases, and I was almost catapulted from one stage to the other, without any initiation on my part. There was something, you might call it "grace," some energy that took me from step to step. I understood how I got the disease, what I was doing to myself to perpetuate it, what kind of people I was attracting that perpetuated the condition, what I needed to do to avoid its recurrence in the future, and what there was for me to learn from this experience so that I could assist others in the future. The visualization continued for quite a while, all the thoughts just coming to me spontaneously and charged with an ecstatic grace; finally, it ended with a powerful vision of Christ, which simply appeared and soon vanished. Then I went to sleep; that was the end of the meditation. The next morning I just got up out of bed. It just felt like time to get up, because it was sunny outside.

8 SELF-HEALING AND VOLUNTARY CONTROL OF THE BODY

Jack Schwarz

Dr. Elmer Green, of the Menninger Foundation in Topeka, Kansas, an expert on biofeedback and voluntary control in internal states, has said that Jack Schwarz has "one of the greatest talents in the country, and probably in the world, in the realm of voluntary bodily controls." As a young man Schwarz taught himself to perform many feats attributed to Hindu and Muslim fakirs. Many have borne witness to his power to control pain and bleeding voluntarily.

Schwarz has developed a holistic model of human functioning and health, based on his studies and personal experiences in the healing arts of various cultures, systems, and philosophies, synthesized with knowledge from science and psychology. He lectures at many colleges, universities, and other institutions, as well as at professional and lay conferences throughout the nation. He has worked in biofeedback research with Elmer Green at the Menninger Foundation, at the Langley Porter Neuropsychiatric Institute with Kenneth Pelletier, and in diagnostics with Paul Grof at McMaster University. He is the author of The Path of Action, *and* Voluntary Controls.

In the foilowing article Mr. Schwarz shares with us his unique insight into his world, and the world of pain and its control.

PAIN IS A NECESSITY, but it can be controlled as soon as we realize what is causing it. By acting upon it and being totally nonattached, we can see the body as a vehicle which is in need of harmonizing. Harmonizing can only be done by raising its vibrational rate and allowing the energy to flow. If you let the traumatic aspect of the pain continue, and if you become attached to the pain, your energy will stagnate, and that stagnation by itself can cause disease.

*Jack
Schwarz*

Patricia Fearey

I experience pain, but I also feel that it's ridiculous to allow something warning you of a disharmony in your life to continue, and to become attached to the warning signal. Compare it with an alarm clock. If I set my alarm clock for seven tomorrow morning, and at seven o'clock it starts ringing, the first thing I do after I open my eyes is shut the clock off. Now it would be ridiculous, once I am out of bed, for that clock to keep ringing, saying "Get up! Get up! Get up!" Pain is in the same way an alarm system.

When I was in the Menninger Foundation the first time to do research there, one of the first things I was asked to do was to put a needle in my arm and show that it wouldn't bleed. Their person with the videotape recorder was zooming back and forth, the PR man next to me was asking all kinds of questions for his newspaper article, and Dr. Elmer Green was running around testing the instruments. Suddenly he handed me the needle, and asked, "Jack, do you *think* that it will bleed?" I heard myself say, "No, I don't *think* so." It was not a positive answer that I gave. I put the needle in, and was asked after a couple of minutes to take it out. Since I had said "I don't *think* it will bleed," it sure enough bled. About two and a half cubic centimeters of blood came out.

Elmer said to me, "Well, at least now I know you can bleed and you don't have vinegar in your veins. Can you do it again?"

I stopped for a couple of seconds and didn't answer him, then said, "Yes, now I will do it without bleeding." I did it again, and no blood came out. Since that time no blood has come out if I don't want to bleed. But when I say, "Now I want it to bleed," I just have to think about it.

Why did it bleed the first time? Because I started to think. For one second, the thought came up, "What if this time, after 33 years of doing it and not bleeding, it does bleed? I will lose my image. I am here in the world-famous Menninger Foundation. Here comes Jack Schwarz, who says he can do it, and now he's going to fail. So he loses his image." The problem is being afraid of losing an image once we have achieved it. By becoming non-attached, I *know* that I'm going to put the needle through my arm, but I also know that it doesn't need to bleed or feel pain.

It would be a totally different story if you stood behind me and without warning suddenly stabbed me. In that case, if I was connected to all the physiological measuring instruments, I would show the traumatic shock you would expect to see. The heart would go faster, the EMT would change, the GSR would change. But if I know that it's going to happen, I also know there doesn't need to be any pain, and the physiological instruments definitely show no indication that my body is being brought into disharmony. The body continues to function through this so-called voluntary control because I know that it will continue to operate and function properly. I have to become totally nonattached. Therefore, I am not putting a needle through *my* arm. I am putting a needle through *an* arm, which happens to be on *a* body, which I just happen to temporarily use as a vehicle. So, actually, there is a loss of personal identification with that part of the body which is being injured.

Much more important than pain control is infection control. The needle I demonstrate pain control with is never sterilized. It has even been put in infected tissue, so that I am injecting bacteria into my body. In all these years, not one single infection has ever occurred, even when I was doing it many times a day with unsterilized instruments. Because of the tremendous high energy, there is no chance for the lower-energy bacteria to affect the body. Sometimes the body cannot maintain its energy level; it becomes exhausted in fighting foreign substances, free radicals, bacteria, and other microorganisms which attack the body. If you could maintain such a high energy field that nothing of a lower nature could enter in, that would be prevention. This is why it is important to maintain high energy under all circumstances. You never know when you're going to be involved in an accident or be exposed to so-called "harmful" bacteria. What I demonstrate works not only in a laboratory, but also in real life accidents, where I have had to immediately put these methods to work.

Every night before I go into meditation, I realize that my meditation will be disturbed by problems I haven't solved yet. So I create a kind of movie, like a daily newscast, in which I and my environment become the main participants. I project the events of the day, not necessarily in chronological order, but as highlights, and I observe what is happening in them. If I see something happening which I think is negative, I immediately stop the movie and observe it even closer.

Let us assume that I suddenly threw a curse word at you, showing my irritation at you. I may have been doing this for years, cursing everybody who did something I didn't like. Perhaps tonight I *see* this for the first time. And I say, "Aha! Thank you for showing me that this is not the way to deal with it, I'm actually trying to make you a victim of my irritation, because I couldn't handle the situation. Why do I make you a victim of that?"

Now, I could call you up and say, "Do you remember what I did to you this afternoon? Well, I didn't really mean to. So I hope you will forgive me." But actually I would thus be pushing the responsibility for what I did upon your shoulders, starting your wounds bleeding again when you had already forgotten the incident, putting the responsibility on you rather than realizing I'm the one who has to deal with it.

From now on, I cannot say any more, "I didn't know I was doing it." Tomorrow, if that same situation occurs with somebody else, instead of cursing, I recognize that I can handle it. I become nonattached. I don't allow myself to become irritated. I don't blame myself for what I've done wrong. I don't start feeling guilty because I did this to you and thereby block my growth. My mistake should be a stepping stone to growth, not a brick on the wall of guilt by which I close myself off from the rest of the world. So tomorrow night when I have my review, I'll see myself acting differently, that the negative has now become a positive.

I don't get excited that I did something good in this. There's no judgment involved. Since I do this review every day, I don't have problems to take with me into my unconscious when I go to bed. That is one of the reasons I can sleep for only two hours. I don't need to dream as many hours trying to unconsciously solve problems I was unable to solve while awake. Trying to deal with feelings of guilt, shame, or blame in the sleep state would hold me back from reenergizing my body and mind.

To me, life is being alive, not just being in a body per se. This is a period of life in which I have to be in a certain form in order to learn, in order to express, in order to bring a specific quality of energy into function. When I say I want to die through meditation, it means I want to be aware of that process of transformation, so that I don't start failing to realize that I have changed through meditation, that I am a new Jack Schwarz. I might not physically look different, because the change might be minute physiologically. I know I have activated energies within me which regenerate part of my body and give it the freedom to start moving more easily. When I die, I come out as a new personality. I have added to my personality; so it might not be completely recognizable any more. I might behave differently, because I don't think I need to go through the same lesson over and over again. Once I know the lesson, I can move on.

We are very progressive beings. Our unconscious continually progresses. Through meditation we both activate and release energies. By becoming aware of them, we actually give them the opportunity to free themselves and to bring regenerative capacities in the body. I feel that life in this physical form continues until all these aspects have been expressed, have been creatively brought into function. I don't believe that anything within the physical human being should ever atrophy, which happens when it is not being used because of a lack of awareness. If I have a tumor somewhere, I want that tumor to die so that it can create new energy and new cells. If I think back on my own life, the reason I can be joyful now is because I experienced a lot of sadness and suffering. After I had gone through it, I saw that I had broken walls down, which let me see some light. When you see just one little speck of light, like a small star on your horizon, it gives you immediately such a tremendous feeling of joy that you can't let go of it.

There are many points in my life I could say are not very joyful. However, when I look at them, I can make joy out of them. Let us assume I don't like spinach, and I find myself eating spinach. I might not get joy out of the spinach, but I certainly get joy out of the fact that I can overcome my dislike for spinach.

People ask, "How can you be joyful in such a world, so full of negatives, so full of sad things? You see people practically dying from terminal diseases. How can you give those people joy?" Well, they might not find joy because of the state they're in; but if they know this is a state through which they have to move in order to achieve a higher state, their outlook upon it can then become joyful. Pain is not something to avoid, but something to recognize and deal with; dealing with it then leads to joy.

When you're dealing with people who are in a deeply depressed state, it's not so much what you can say to them that is important, but the atmosphere you create about them. Then you can show them some of the power they themselves have. Most of the time they have been told that nothing can be done. That expands their despair and hopelessness, and might even cause a lack of will to live. Quite often people have unexplored capacities. If we can show them some of the potentials they have never touched upon, they might be able to grab onto them as a last resort. We can give them a method by which they can explore these potentials and work with them. For instance, we use methods by which they start learning to visualize a new and better situation outside themselves. By exploring that new vision and becoming involved in it, they let go, and thus become nonattached from this physiological state, this diseased state. In this way they actually activate a lot of energy without consciously working on the body at all. By working with that tremendous energy outside of themselves, they begin to reflect it, and a generative healing process starts taking place within the body.

Joy comes then from the feeling that they have done something for themselves, instead of depending on someone else to do it for them. The healing power is in them, and it is their choice to take that healing power and do something with it. It comes down again to the word "responsibility," not only for themselves, but for mankind. They have a duty toward their fellow man to bring out their capacities and their potentials, which are blocked within the disease. We can give them methods by which they can unblock these capacities. We can give them a chance to discover this process for themselves. Remarkable things result from this. People you would not expect to be very happy or joyful, because they have such a terrible disease, suddenly start changing and bringing out their artistry and their potentials, and they start living again. Through that, healing already starts taking place.

When we start transforming our being through greater awareness, we should realize that the body, which is the vehicle through which we should express this new consciousness, requires an intake of the proper foods and the proper ingredients. We are electrochemical beings, and quite often we are hampered by psychosomatic diseases, which means that the mind is not allowing the body to function properly. We have some other psychic diseases, too, when the body is not sufficiently nourished and doesn't stay in homeostasis. Either we have too much or we have too little, which can happen quite easily when we don't get proper nutrition. We need to realize that when we have a deficiency of some nutrient in the body, we also at the same time have an excess of another substance that needs to interact with it.

It is essential that we start looking at nutrition individually and not just assuming that if we're on a certain diet, we're okay. We need to see what the individual's needs are. If a person has an expanded growth pattern, then his or her body needs more help. The mind can do anything, being a very powerful instrument, but it needs ingredients and substances on which to work. Therefore proper nutrition is a necessity. I'm convinced that if people had a better understanding of what the body needed, they could avoid all kinds of mental aberrations and physiological problems.

When considering nutrition, we are better off using natural substances, which already have the intrinsic factors of life in them, than using any of the synthetics. The nutritional ingredients in food are activators of the different organs, which start distributing the energies and keeping the homeostatic balance of the body going. We see, for instance, people who get into a tremendous state of depression for no reason at all. They don't know why they are depressed. Suddenly they cannot handle being with other people any more. They start crying, they become hysterical, they get feelings of despair, and sometimes even become suicidal. If you look at some of the other symptoms they have, you might find that their gums become very tender, that they get slight physical tics in their eyes, they get humming and ringing in the ears, they get itching all over their bodies, and they have sore joints. There are about 150 symptoms I can think of right offhand, where the only problem they actually have is a lack of potassium. Their bodies might even tell them "Eat bananas," because bananas are a good source of potassium. But they don't pay attention to that. They just think they're craving bananas, and might even eat a couple, which will temporarily replenish the potassium, but after a little while it is exhausted again.

For years I've been talking about the body's need for copper and zinc. When I started telling people ten years ago they needed zinc, they would say, "Come on, that's good for gutters." Then I would talk about copper, and would be told, "Well, it is good for copper pipes in the plumbing. How did you get this crazy idea?" Now, science has started to realize how very important these elements are in the body.

It is logical that if you give these elements in heavy molecular form, and the body already lacks energy, it may not always be able to break it down and assimilate it properly. We need to question if there are less dense forms of these substances available. The homeopathic remedies have a tremendous value, because they are triturated in a form that is taken out of the molecular structure and put into an ionic structure. In this form it is much easier for the body to assimilate than in a chemical, molecular state, and will have a faster effect on the body. Also, when we take vitamins we should be aware that they cannot operate unless we have the proper elements and trace elements in our body. We, therefore, again have to look at the individual needs of the person.

Lately we have become aware that the blood test tells you very little. Your blood might contain all the ingredients your body needs, but it might be just trucking them through your body without ever delivering them to the tissues or to the organs. So we need to start looking for another way to find out if the tissues and the organs are getting these substances. There are now new tests, such as hair tests, which are not perfect yet, but which at least give you a better indication of what a person is lacking.

We have to find methods by which we can "diagnose" what is happening in a person. The manner which I use is by looking at the energy fields surrounding a person. We have been indoctrinated that auras are not visible, and that only some "psychic" people can see them, which is nonsense. We can all be trained to observe the energy fields, if we get away from believing that we can see only the so-called "visible" spectrum. By observing the energy fields, we can become aware of what the person's symptoms are. Thus, if we know what is happening, we also know what ingredients are lacking or in excess, and throwing this electrochemical balance off. It is a discipline to be always very much aware of what a body is saying to you, to recognize that it is telling you what its needs are. It's also telling you what its wants are, and you have to realize the difference between the two. In the Western world, we have made needs of our wants. Every time we hear a want, we claim it is a need. As a result, we in the countries of the Western world take the most from the Earth, put the least back, and are still the most malnourished people in the whole world, not because we eat less—we eat more—but because we don't eat the proper things, because we don't listen to what the body tells us. So it's a discipline, to be willing to listen to what your body's actual needs are and to distinguish them from your wants.

9 THINKING HEALTHILY
Irving Oyle, O.D.

Irving Oyle is a Doctor of Osteopathic Medicine. He organized New York City's first free clinic, and after moving west in 1970, founded a holistic health clinic in Bolinas, California. The Bolinas Headland Clinic incorporated herbal medicine, osteopathy, traditional medicine, psychic healing and acupressure. During this period, Dr. Oyle developed sonopuncture, a technique that uses high-frequency sound rather than needles in the acupuncture points of the body.

Dr. Oyle is a well-known writer on health. His books include The Healing Mind, *and* Magic, Mysticism, Modern Medicine. *He is known as a lecturer, and his philosophy of healing is thought to be on the forefront of our knowledge of the human mind and body.*

Dr. Oyle, in this article, shares with us his ideas that the mind and the body are one, that healing comes from within the self, and that attitude about the causes of disease plays an important part in eliminating illness. Imagery and guided fantasy have a place in self-healing. The practitioners of healing work in co-operation with the "patient" to neutralize the spiritual, mental, and physical diseases, so that true inner healing can take place.

THE INTEREST IN HOLISTIC HEALTH is a natural growth within the evolution of the healing arts. It started with Hippocrates; recently it has taken another step. I've been doing my own research to see what is actually responsible for healing in people. My colleagues and I have looked into such things as biofeedback, visual imagery, Chinese acupuncture, sonic acupuncture (using high-frequency sound instead of needles), looking for something that will tie the whole healing process together. I would say that the patient's attitude about what is responsible for the disease is a large factor in eliminating it. We, as physicians, make the mistake of thinking we're treating *a* body. There's a certain presumption made there, reminiscent of the "world is flat" presumption. In my opinion, there is not one shred of proof that there is such a thing as a physical body.

Immanuel Kant suggested that time and space are figments of our imagination. It's entirely possible that the whole reality you see is only hapening on the back of your eyeballs, that there isn't anybody out there but you, and that you're making the whole thing up. Most of us are conditioned by the Cartesian presumption that there is a real physical world to which we have to adapt by means of our mental and emotional apparatus. These days that's a shaky presumption at best.

Albert Einstein suggested that matter and energy are two aspects of a single phenomena. The Hindus and the Buddhists suggest that mind, energy, and matter are but three aspects of a single phenomenon, somewhat like a trinity. We've been, for the last two or three hundred years, hung up on maniuplating matter. It's a holdover from Newtonian physics.

Most of the people in the healing professions never caught on to Einstein's suggestion that energy and matter are separate forms of a single entity. In looking to get what we call healing, we can interfere on the energy level by using something like acupuncture, as well as on the consciousness level by introducing new views of reality. When we interfere with consciousness, for example, by proposing that there really is nothing out there, that requires a huge change in consciousness. We've always been told that you have to treat organic disease, that you have to make the patient feel better. These days it doesn't make any difference whether he feels better or not, the doctor must produce some definite laboratory evidence that the disease is gone.

Some eminent American authorities are saying about acupuncture anesthesia, "Well, it's just hypnosis. You've hypnotized the patient." They presume that if you use acupuncture, and the patient feels no pain, that doesn't mean that the pain isn't there. The pain is still there even though nobody is feeling it. These authorities argue that we have to continue to concern ourselves with "curing" organic disease. I would like to suggest

*Irving
Oyle*

Paul Schraub

that we need concern ourselves only with what the patient *thinks* he has. As physicians, we really have no right to say, "It doesn't matter what you think you have, *I* know what you've got."

There is a movement within the medical profession to use this so-called "mind over matter" approach. Carl Jung, the great psychoanalyst, pioneered in this area with his method of active imagination. We might also call him a modern-day alchemist, who suggested that when one talks about converting lead into gold, the lead and the gold are actually the same thing. As an analogy, assume that the lead is the physical symptom that the patient complains about. We've been taught that our purpose is to suppress the symptom. However, perhaps we can convert the energy in the symptom into the cure, simply by reversing its polarity. Jung had a method for doing this, and that's one of the methods we've been researching.

We've been working with a process of converting the symptom into a mental image. As the symptom "becomes" a mental image, the patient can talk to this mental image, and the image tells the patient what is going wrong. The patient sees the symptom as a signal from the body that something is off. We should decipher that signal, tune into it, listen in to it, look at it, and get the message from it, instead of knocking out the message, which is the usual approach.

Suppose I have a patient who has a pain in his buttock. Upon examination, I see that the reason he has a pain in his buttock is because he's sitting on a tack. Using the current medical approach, I would give him half a grain of morphine every three of four hours, and maybe perk it down with codeine, and allow him to continue to sit on the tack. It's time to get people up off their rear ends and off the tack, and allow them to understand that, if they have a symptom, it's trying to tell them something.

The technique I use to stimulate visual imagery uses acupuncture to induce an alpha state in which the patient stops linear thinking. I usually employ some breathing exercises in order to raise the oxygen content so the patients feel better. Then I suggest that they imagine themselves in a very beautiful place. This works especially well with meditators, artists, and other people whose creative side is well-developed, who can make images.

I tell them to hang out in this very beautiful place, and pretty soon they will see some living creature, either an animal or a person. They should greet the animal or person, and make friends, then ask the new-found friend about the illness. Invariably the fantasy image tells them what is going wrong. This process is generally called guided imagery.

I once did a demonstration of this technique for some mental-health people in Santa Cruz. There was a young woman there who'd been under treatment for four years for cancer phobia. She was sure she had cancer, and they had been unable to convince her otherwise. However, she was a good visualizer. I said, "Imagine yourself in a beautiful place." She said, "Okay, I'm there." She imagined herself in a forest, and as she described the trees and the path, she suddenly said, "Oh, look, I see a deer." I said, "Find out his name." She found out the deer's name; it was a female. Then I said, "Ask the deer about your cancer." The deer said, "Don't be stupid, you don't have cancer." That was it; she believed the deer.

About three days later, I got a call from the Commissioner of Mental Health in Santa Cruz telling me some of the department heads were upset. They were worried about being replaced by a deer.

The body is a fantastic machine, able to heal itself. I think that healing is something we have to actively inhibit. We assume that someone or something must cause the healing: I have to heal you, or you have to heal yourself. Essentially, all you have to do is get out of the way, and permit the healing to take place. There are inhibitory processes, or cramps, which, by simply being released, allow the body to flow and to heal normally. We have to understand that none of us actually does any healing. It seems almost like arrogance to think that we heal anybody, or cure anybody. All we do is set up the conditions under which healing takes place.

Death has been described as the ultimate disease. But let's look at a fetus at term, nine months. What have you got? A water-dwelling creature attached by a stalk to a nourishing soil which for nine months has been pumping blood in. What happens at birth? The water is let out, the roof is ripped off, and the little creature is flung out into an alien atmosphere. That's more like death than birth.

What we call disease is probably, insofar as we control it, a refusal to be reborn. In order to be healed, you have to be reborn into a new state of consciousness. Disease is a call to higher consciousness. When I see somebody who's really sick, I wonder, what is that disease preventing the person from doing? How is the disease changing the person's life? The disease can point a direction in which you can go.

10 OVERCOMING DUALISM
Patricia Sun

Patricia Sun, among other things, uses her own psychic abilities to catalyze natural healing capabilities in others. In her workshops she deals with the experience of feeling healing and transcendent concepts, with sound as a healing force, as well as with movement, breathing, meditation, and ways of unblocking personal energy. Graduating Phi Beta Kappa from the University of California, she earned two degrees in 3½ years, in Conservation and Natural Resources, and in Psychology, and practiced Family Counseling for a time. With her strong background in science, she came into "psychic" healing with great hesitancy, finally acknowledging her gift to open herself to the intuitive force of total unrelenting love, which is the hallmark of the experience in her workshops.

The integration of spiritual healing with the body and mind are particularly focused in Patricia Sun's healing work. She is internationally known for her ability to channel healing energy through vocal sounds. The sounds that come from Patricia are deeply moving. Those who have worked with her feel they have been healed physically and spiritually.

Patricia Sun, like many gifted healers and psychics, has often been quoted and written about, but seldom have her own words appeared in print. This article offers us a unique opportunity to understand and explore Patricia's own experiences and thoughts about her work.

DIFFERENCES BETWEEN THE RIGHT AND LEFT sides of the body have been significant for many thousands of years to many cultures. Especially the Eastern and the Egyptian cultures were

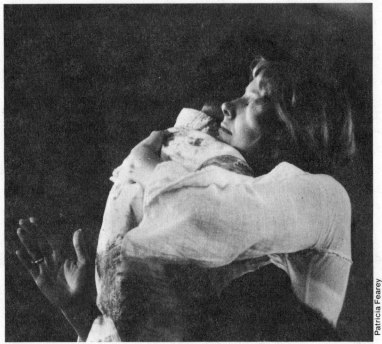

Patricia Fearey

Patricia Sun

concerned with these differences, both in medicine and in philosophy. Now, we here in the West have discovered that the right and left hemispheres of the brain control opposite sides of the body; the right brain controls the operations of the left side, the left brain controls the operations of the right side. The ancient tradition was that the left side of the body was the feminine side: the yin, the receptive, the void, the acausal, the not-logical, the place where messages from God come through. Cause and effect did not operate here; concepts just pop up in nonlinear fashion. "Yin" is the Chinese word for this energy in all its aspects.

The right side of the body is "yang." It is masculine, and has to do with being linear, linguistic, rational, logical, dynamic, and assertive. These are the two polarities of energy, and we each contain these polarities in our body. Consequently, when you experience an illness or symptom on the right side of your body, it may be related to your dynamic assertive energy, your "yang"energy. Conversely, when the problem is on the left side, it probably relates to your ability to be receptive.

Our muscles hold energy. That's why our spines get crooked, and we slouch. Each of us has a different kind of posture, because the muscles have contracted from holding so much energy, and the skeletal system has been pulled out of line. I connect all physical problems with energy held in the body. This "held" energy comes about in many different kinds of ways: sometimes through psychic trauma or through psychological tension.

Consciousness and Duality

All consciousness *expansion* comes about through the experience of *limitation.* We can experience a window as a window only because it has borders. If there were no borders, everything would be known, and nothing would be known. Duality would be gone; there would be nothing, just as before the beginning, there was nothing. So God created something. He created the duality game in us. We are it.

The only reason we're not expressing and being all that we can be is because we've bought as truths our limited view of truth. We've been programmed and conditioned psychically with the unconscious fears of our parents and family, our associates and our entire mass culture. Each of us in a body has been powerfully programmed. Nobody escapes it. Each of us absorbs the collective unconscious in our own special way, given the particular point in time and space that we come into being here. We are primarily a sponge from the moment of conception through the first seven years of our lives, complexly absorbing unconscious energy dynamics. A major part of what we absorb is unsated fear. We live in terror of things that we have never experienced. A lot of pain and suffering results from these fears. We're still like a child who is afraid there's a bogeyman in the room because he sees a shadow move. His terror can be so overwhelming that he can actually leap out the window and break his leg. We all know there's no bogeyman; yet we also know that when we feel fear we often do get a broken leg, which thus reinforces our fears, and "proves" them.

Of course, all suffering has to do with duality, with the tearing of consciousness by right/wrong, not seeing the continuum, but having it either/or. If you're suffering, you must be bad; for in dualistic thinking, you cannot believe that you are good. You cannot *be* good if there is some bad; and so you are trapped, for there is always some bad. The thing to know to transcend duality is that the "bad" (and problems) are the growing edge of discovery, i.e., the *un*covering of consciousness. So it is good to have a growing edge which expands consciousness in the universe. And when we can hold that, we have transcended duality and hold the paradox, which is all good.

We live in a dualistic world with a dualistic consciousness: left/right, male/female, good/bad. It's set up to be one or the other. We're now learning to integrate the two opposites, to allow for the experience of the two things to be present at the same time. Nothing can function as only one thing. It's all part of our mythical set. I have a vision that we are each evolving beings with evolving consciousnesses as well. We handle one aspect of consciousness; then let it go dormant while we handle another aspect; and we keep going back and forth in a cyclical way. However, each time we go back and forth, we escalate upward.

These days we have a problem even in speaking, because our language is born out of the oppositions of either/or; left/right; male/female; good/bad; is it or isn't it? We feel safe and comfortable when we're on one side or the other. If it's "bad," you can throw it out. If it's "good," you can want it. It's difficult for Westerners to understand duality.

Yet, that difficulty is precisely the place where we are transforming our consciousness, where we are expanding our intelligence, our ability to be creative, our ability to perceive, and our ability to use all our natural, inherent talents. We sense we have these talents, but they get blocked off. We block them off by putting them in one box or the other, rather than creating an immense box that allows all of them to be there at the same time. All our mundane problems and pains, all our difficulties between men and women in marriage, in work, in families, all are born of these boxes.

The Bible says when Adam and Eve ate from the tree of the knowledge of good and evil, then they knew shame. When we split up and became two things, when we entered the duality game, things became either/or. In that way, if it wasn't good, it was bad. Then we had to have shame. Now we're trying to find solutions to our problems where everybody wins. I can be right, and I can say something different from you; and you can be right, and you can say something different from me. And we can both expand and grow and feel good, you saying one thing, me saying another. There is no reason why there has to be a conflict. I've often felt that the only reason people ever disagreed on anything was because they didn't communicate long enough. They didn't get a box big enough to hold all the parts.

Remember, what we are doing here is expanding consciousness and perceiving more of what the universe is about. That's our purpose. We bring love and value and an appreciation of life into all experience. We can have reverence for life and eat meat. We can have reverence for life and eat, period, because I contend that plants are as conscious as animals in their own way. We can participate in life, have reverence for life, and still live off life. There's no way we can do anything else. That's the way the game is set up. It's part of the paradox. Comprehending the paradox is the point of power in consciousness.

We can participate in life in a way that lets everything happen. It's a combination of the metaphysical and the rational that makes everything work. Albert Einstein revealed the deeply spiritual side of his own nature when he said;

> "The most beautiful and profound emotion we can experience is the sensation of the mystical. It is the sower of all true science. He to whom this emotion is a stranger, who can no longer wonder and stand rapt in awe, is as good as dead. To know that what is impenetrable to us really exists manifesting itself as the highest wisdom and the most radiant beauty which our dull faculties can comprehend only in their primitive forms, this knowledge, this feeling, is at the center of true religiousness."

Of course, most great scientists will say that the things they discovered more or less popped in on them, or just fell together. It's the "Aha" or "Eureka" experience. It just clicks. They present a problem from the rational, dynamic side, and then they open up to the other side, the impenetrable, the more, the all. We open up into there, and things move in. We will always have the duality game; we'll still be going back and forth. Eventually, it will be so full that it will be simultaneously separate and together.

We will operate in the consciousness beyond duality, where we will be much more conscious, and won't have to have that old bogeyman, demonic, suffering stuff in such a dead and paralyzing way.

Rather, that life is uncannily beautiful: all we need do is pay attention to our life and what problems come up in it. The problems are not an accident. A problem in life is a place where we are letting go of old conditioning and moving into an expanded place.

Two major mechanisms have been very useful and powerful for me. One is to remember to realize that we are part of a greater whole. Remember that the universe is unfolding as it should. Remember that everything is okay. We don't even have to believe it. If we just start to consider it, we will have shifted our energy perspective in the world. That begins to blow conditioning tapes immediately.

The second mechanism involves taking on what's happening to us in a very responsible way. It is realizing that all the energy that surrounds us—the problems, the people, the circumstances—is a metaphor for energy we are clarifying within ourselves. We can begin to see everyone as our mirror. People we don't like, things we don't like, our attachment to hating them or disliking what they do, all give us clues about what we are working on seeing or letting go.

At a deeper level, we begin to learn how to love ourselves. We can take responsibility for it in such a way that we are able to respond. We give ourselves an opportunity to realize that we don't have to hate that person or that situation. There are ways to respond that are not helpless or stuck in loss. We can also begin to expand our compassion, our ability to perceive our oneness with even that person we dislike. It is not simply "There but for the grace of God go I." It is, "There *by* the grace of God go I." If we can really get that there is a meaning for everyone's life, we can understand how everyone is different from us, and everyone is the same as us.

Before we can freely, without barriers, actually perceive our oneness with everyone, we must first acknowledge, love, and respect our own uniqueness. When we really experience that, we realize we're not in competition with anyone. We're going to do it our own way, and the way we want to do it will be what is good. The way we become a success in the world is by being who we are, not trying to be like someone else who was a success in the world.

Synergy and Creativity

Synergy is a concept that postulates that the whole is more than the sum of its parts. therefore, when we are only visualizing or experiencing each thing as a part, we don't receive the total energy available. However, when all is communicated together at once, there's an alchemy, an actual transition in perception and interaction, a transformation into something else that is more than the sum of the parts. We are moving to a more-than-the-sum-of-the-parts-place in our consciousness and in our interactions with each other. By becoming very clear about our microcosm of self, we are beginning to perceive the macrocosm in a more profound way.

Gradually, we're each finding a way to have both the intuitive, acausal side and the rational, logical side of our brain functioning simultaneously. It's like the image of "duration" in the *I Ching*. The rousing thunder and the gentle wind each sustain the other. One is impossible without the other. When both are given their due, the duration of the universe unfolds. We can allow these two parts of ourselves to coexist, where we can "hear voices" and be comfortable in hearing them, and, at the same time, be rational and logical, exercising our linear, conceptual abilities. If we allow them to feed and sustain each other, we move to a very creative and powerful place.

I believe all true creativity comes from such a process. Even as a child I think I knew that. The theory of relativity came about through such a process: pondering it, playing with it, just letting it sort of percolate. Abraham Maslow was one of the few psychologists willing to look at creative people to see what they were about. He found they always had this ability to let both parts of themselves function when they were doing their creative work. He called them self-actualized individuals.

This creative process means not fearing what we experience, not censoring what floats into our heads. Our main censor always tells us: "Watch out! It's demonic. You'll get possessed. Something bad will happen. You'll go crazy. You won't be in control. You won't stay on purpose and get your job done. It's not good. It's not right." Consequently we're constantly invalidating many experiences that are beginning to rise into our consciousness.

Apparently, my function is to create the room and safety for others to look at the fear long enough to dissolve it, so that they can get to an integrated place without having to bar any experience. Because fear is what makes you ill; fear is what destroys your creativity. We are all creative, and creativity is that alchemy of letting those aspects of our unique selves flow.

The Healing Sounds

When I first started making the sounds, people would ask me,"Where do the sounds come from?" The answer I gave then was fairly naive and spontaneous: "They seem to just come out of an old place." They seemed old to me; "primordial" was the word that came to mind. I've had many experiences since then which are beginning to explain the sounds to some degree. However, I don't think they are fully explained yet.

From a more low-key, rational point of view, the sounds are a vibration. There is even one theory that all matter is only vibration; everything, even the first energy, was and is vibration, even before there was light. Interestingly enough, the Bible says, "In the beginning was the Word," and the first words spoken were "Let there be light." It is as though one created the other. I had a sense of that, totally in myself, even before I noticed the correlation to the Bible references and current physics theories about the origins of the universe.

Sounds, as vibration, affect our physical bodies. From what I personally experience subjectively, from what others report and what I intuit they are feeling, there seems to be a balancing of energy, a centering where discordant vibrations in the body get tuned. This "tuning" allows the frequency of the body's vibrations to rise comfortably. There is some research that indicates that pure compounded, specially pitched sounds synchronize the left and right brainwave patterns. I'm quite interested in that analysis, because it ties in with so much of the verbiage that I use regarding duality and the synchronization of energy.

I trust the sounds that I make because they are very centering and healing to me personally. I sort of get lost in them, not thinking about them when I make them. I must say, I do experience them as holy. I just tend to ride with them. I can think about them somewhat, but basically, when they're really good and I'm really into them, me, Patricia Sun, is somewhere else. I'm just being the sound.

For information on Patricia Sun's workshops and healing work, write to her at P.O. Box 7065, Berkeley, CA 94707, or phone (415) 524-5795.

4 THE LIFE CYCLE

THE CYCLE OF LIFE—to be born, to be a child, to grow into adulthood, to mature, to grow old, to die—is a series of rites of passage shared by all. Each of these transitions in time calls for change, which we experience in the body, the mind, and the spirit.

Life is lived through these passages. We meet the challenge of ourselves in each phase of the cycle. To grow as a human being is to go through this cycle successfully.

In the United States, we share unrealistic feelings about youth. The media, movies, TV, books, magazines, the papers, add to the myth that the only place to be in life is at the stage of the young adult: be one of the beautiful people; be 16 forever. This misconception, coupled with Western medicine's odd idea that these stages of transition are unhealthy, has led us to be uncomfortable around birth, aging, and death.

In this section we have included articles on childbirth, aging and stress, and dying. These phases of our life are the ones most often mishandled because of our unrealistic concepts about the cycle and by Western medical practices. The New Healers, in the practice of holistic health, have helped us gracefully transfer from one stage to another. They see the phases of the life cycle as being normal, not a type of illness or disease.

Dr. Frederic LeBoyer, in his humanistic work with childbirthing, has introduced to the Western society the idea that newborn infants have emotions, and that those emotions must be considered at the time of birthing by those assisting at the birth. His techniques of handling the newborn child at the time of delivery are contrary to the usual hospital practices. Dr. LeBoyer emphasises safety for both mother and child in an atmosphere of nonviolence.

"Growing Older," by Ken Dychtwald, discusses his views on aging and personal growth. Dr. Dychtwald, President of the Association for Humanistic Gerontology and former Director of the SAGE Project, shares with us his insight that cultural beliefs can profoundly affect the quality of aging.

Charles Garfield, Clinical Professor in Medical Psychology at the Cancer Research Center in San Francisco, shares with us his insight and experience in working with dying people, as they transit from life to death. His perspective shows us that people need a sense of direction in their lives regardless of their spiritual development or station in life.

A.P.K.

11 HOLISTIC CHILDBIRTH
Frederic LeBoyer, M.D.

Frederic LeBoyer, M.D., graduated from the School of Medicine, University of Paris, where he became Chef de Clinique in 1954-55 before devoting himself completely to his obstetrical practice. During his career as an obstetrician, he delivered 9,000 babies by conventional means. After years of observing the infants' agonizing experience and then reexperiencing his own birth trauma through psychotherapy, Dr. LeBoyer recognized the emotional trauma in the technologically competent and commonly accepted procedures of childbirth, which grossly neglect the emotional needs of the sensitive newborn infant. By patient attention to relieving the birth trauma, Dr. LeBoyer learned that the violent crying is unnecessary and that, instead, the birth process can be a gentle "love affair." He thus concludes that the first few minutes after delivery, which are so important in determining the individual's orientation toward life, should be an experience of loving communication rather than of isolated distress. He has since delivered over 1,000 babies with the new orientation of warmth and sensitivity, and research indicates that they are exceptional in many ways.

Since the publication of his book Birth Without Violence, *the LeBoyer method of childbirth has become an international cause among natural-childbirth proponents. Today, there are trained practitioners in the United States, who practice, and train others in, the LeBoyer method of birthing.*

Dr. LeBoyer's insight into childbirth, families, and health care gives us a gentle and humane way of entering life. His ideas on maternal and infant care, and the effects of birthing on the personality of the child, are thought-provoking.

*Frederic
LeBoyer*

courtesy of F. LeBoyer

THE NEWBORN BABY is not at all the unconscious little thing we
have assumed it to be for such a long time. We assumed that a
newborn baby doesn't feel, doesn't see, doesn't hear, has no emotions. It is just the opposite.

I would say that our conditioning is a sort of diaphragm. We
see only what we are interested in seeing. For instance, if you are
interested in building houses, when you travel in the country you
will say, "Oh, I can build a home here; it will go like this and like
that." If you are in real estate you say, "Oh, with this land I could
do this and that." If you are a painter, you will say, "Oh, I could
make a painting in such a way." If you are a military man, you
say, "I could put my guns here and so." We have a view of things
which depends entirely on our frame of mind, how we have been
brought up, and what our interests are in life. We are conditioned
by education, by culture, and mostly by language. If we want to
recapture unconditioned consciousness, we must go back to the

condition of the newborn child. There is no such conditioning in a baby.

A baby still has a consciousness which is wide open, not conditioned, and this is what is making birth so traumatic. This consciousness is unprotected. The baby takes in everything without discrimination. In a way, the consciousness of a newborn baby is very close to the consciousness of the hypnotic state, in which there is no checking, no discriminating, and no selecting. Everything is taken in without any control. Simply stated, the input stimuli are tremendous. There is no filtering, no screening. Everything comes in.

When I started reflecting about birth, I was trying to see how we could reduce this tremendous trauma for the child. Always working with this very simple idea, I said to myself, "All we've got to do is to give new sensations, not of life, of course, because the baby was alive before he was born, but of this environment in which we are living, as progressively as possible and with the lowest intensity." My point of view was more that of a teacher; I was much more concerned with education than with medicine, because after all, the first few minutes of birth are a lesson. We are expected to learn within a few minutes all that life is going to give us. We are expected to assimilate and integrate all the new sensations of this outer life.

Any teacher, or anyone who is interested in education, knows very well that we can only take in a very little at a time. We have to digest it, integrate it, and then we can take some more. Everyone remembers how long it took to learn writing or reading, or to develop the simple movements of any practical skill. We understand that this process of assimilating information takes a very long time. So we should give to this child only as much as he can assimilate and integrate. And being born is the first lesson.

The senses of the newborn baby are so open, so sensitive, so sharp that, in my system, all stimuli must be kept as minimal as possible. The child is born in dim light because the eyes are very sensitive. When the child actually comes out, no one talks; there is complete silence in the delivery room. One has to imagine what it is to be touched for the first time, and then understand how carefully this first touching of the baby is to be done. This little spine is so sensitive; this little body is to be handled with very

great precaution and with a deep knowledge of one's own functioning, one's own spine.

I've seen time and again that not only are the babies sensitive
to light, but there is a great sense of discrimination. In order to
have dim light in my delivery room, I had black curtains installed.
Once the baby is placed in water and is fully relaxed, and I feel
that he has accepted all, has even begun to enjoy his new condition, little by little, I lift the curtains, so that just a little light is
allowed in the room. As soon as this daylight is there, immediately the child will turn his head and look at the light. But if, on the
contrary, we switch on electricity, immediately he will close his
eyes, meaning that one light is pleasant and the other one harmful. And if it is flourescent light, the reaction is even stronger. It
is as if the baby is saying, "Oh, this is unbearable. Please switch
it off. Nothing of that for me." These babies know what is good
for them and what is not good. We should follow their lead.

Not only are the senses important, but we must be aware that
our inner emotions are perceived by this newborn baby. I would
say that the newborn child possesses extrasensory perception
functioning to the fullest extent, because the intellect is not
developed yet. There seems to be a conflict between extrasensory perception and intellect. The more the intellect is developed,
the less the extrasensory perception is likely to function.

There is no doubt that the baby is sensitive and responsive to
the moods of the people who are attending the delivery. This I
have been able to witness time and time again. Some people have
asked, "But what proof have you of all this?" The proof is very
simple. It is in the response of the child. If you had observed as
many newborn children as I have, you would know the meaning
of their responses also.

I remember some deliveries when a friend of mine was present. He is a very violent man, very nervous, very impatient.
Whenever he was there, the children would be screaming. When
I would invent some reason to ask him to go away, immediately
the child would calm down. These babies are definitely sensing
all that is going on around them. In the old days it was said that
good and bad fairies were there at the time of birth with good
presents and bad presents. That was nothing but a symbolic way
of saying that the mood of the persons who are present at the

very moment of birth are extremely important. They will leave a sort of imprint on this little one.

We have no screaming anymore. Believe me, fifteen or twenty years ago entering a delivery room was unbearable—screaming, screaming, screaming. Now that is finished; we have other ways of dealing with the mother's suffering. It is really marvelous to watch a delivery going peacefully, quietly, without any of the screaming. But the contrast of this peace and silence with the terrible agony which the baby is experiencing finally struck me. I asked myself, what can we do now for this baby, since we've done only half of the job? With the babies which are born according to these new ideas, there is silence: no crying, no screaming. There is one cry when they come out, which is good and necessary, indicating that the breathing system is functioning normally, but further crying is unnecessary.

I am not denying that oxygen is an absolute must for the newborn baby. Lack of oxygen, even for a few seconds, will damage the brain so much that the child will become a cripple. Physicians are 100 percent right to insist on this. It is their first concern, and that is as it must be. But as long as breathing is normal after this first cry, there may be a second cry, but no more is needed.

After all, why should we scream, and sob, and cry when we are born? There is no practical reason, no more for the child than there is for the mother. For centuries we couldn't see what we could do about the suffering of the mother; so we used to say, "She has to suffer." And similarly we created all kinds of reasons for the baby to cry, such as that crying will strengthen the lungs. Well, the lungs are sound; they don't need strengthening. Or we said "Oh, you have to spank the baby in order to start and stimulate his breathing." No, breathing is there, and you don't have to start it or stimulate it.

The oldest children I have helped deliver by using these new ideas are now about eight years old. All together there are about 1,000 of them, and they seem to be quite different. I don't want to say too much, because I don't know precisely how different they are. Two psychologists from the Sorbonne have been doing a follow-up study which is going to be published this year. These children seem to be happy. I am told that they keep laughing.

They take every thing in a positive way. What is at stake when a child is born is whether the newness will be accepted or whether the child will try to cling to the past, to run away from new experiences—and life is continuously new. These children have been experiencing this newness in such a pleasant way that they are always open to whatever comes. For all intents and purposes, I am told, they do not cry. They have very strong personalities. They possess amazing memories and extraordinary interests and are continuously exploring.

At the beginning, I was wondering whether I was going to have children who are passive and depressed, because people say that aggressiveness is a must in this jungle. No. My opinion is just the opposite. Aggression is always covering fear and sorrow. An elephant is not aggressive, because he is so strong that he has nothing to fear, and when you don't fear anything, you are not aggressive.

Natural childbirth has a tremendous impact on the mother, on all women who have their babies this way. It is all the more striking when they have previously had one or two children. They say, "How is it that all children are not born like this?" What they are going through is so deep that they simply say, "It is beyond words. I can't tell you." This method of childbirth completely changes the relationship between mother and child. The woman discovers suddenly the magnitude of what is taking place. Instead of a purely mechanical process, it is something that is very, very deep. And of course this deep relationship between mother and child certainly has a great importance in the eventual results we can expect from this new person.

I think that the father is very important, but he will come into the picture much later. You see, there are stages of life. We are so impatient that we confuse everything. We have lost this feeling that there are stages of life, and they have to be accepted. If the presence of the father is necessary for the wellbeing of the mother, all right, very good. But basically nothing should disturb this first meeting between mother and child. Of course, very often part of the happiness of the woman is that she is giving a child to her husband. And she might be all the happier since she can share her joy with her husband.

I feel that it is very important to respect the personality of children, to accept that they are little beings with a deep knowledge of many things. The best attitude in education is to accept children as they are, fully valuing all their inner knowledge. Usually we feel that we have to teach everything to children. No. They know by themselves. The best we can do is not to hinder this development.

I feel that women actually have very little self-confidence in this society, not only in America, but Western society as a whole. I keep receiving letters from women saying, "Oh, yes, this way of delivery seems to be so true. Where am I to find someone who is going to deliver my child like this? Where should I go? Can you give me an address?" And I keep saying, "Come back to yourself." No one can eat for you, no one can walk for you, no one can sleep for you, and no one can have this child but you. You are going to have this baby. And it is very strange that gynecologists are saying, "I did a difficult delivery" or "I did a very beautiful delivery." Truly speaking, the one who is doing the delivery is the mother, no one else, and basically she needs nothing. If she is self-confident enough to know that nothing is needed, everything will take its own course; everything will be all right. What need is there of anything else?

Actually, to a large extent all the technology now in hospitals basically is there to make the woman feel secure. Perhaps she could get that feeling of security from something quite different, let us say, religion. In certain countries, for instance, women who are expecting babies go on pilgrimage to holy places, and if they have visited the high places, they feel fully secure. They have no doubt that everything will be all right. But the holy place now is the hospital. Medicine has taken the place of the church. A woman feels, "Oh, yes, there are all these instruments, all that is necessary to help me in case problems arise. Oh yes, I can depend on that." This moral effect is very, very important. It can work the other way also. Personally, I would be terrified by all these instruments. Seeing so many machines for my body, I would say, "Oh, no, no."

I was reading recently where the World Health Organization has released statistics showing a very high rate of prenatal mortality here in this country, where apparently most women have their children in hospitals. The lowest rate is in Holland, where practically all women have home deliveries. I don't mean to say that I am advocating home deliveries. I am only trying to say that things probably are not working exactly as we think.

12 GROWING OLDER
Ken Dychtwald, Ph.D.

Aging is often a misunderstood and feared experience in our society. The problems of aged people have more to do with their being seen as second-class citizens than with their health.

Ken Dychtwald, psychologist, is a leading pioneer in holistic health and the human potential movement. For the past ten years he has been particularly interested in researching ways by which the techniques and philosophies of bodymind development can be effectively integrated into existing health-care programs, counseling services, and fitness/recreation activities. Dr. Dychtwald is President of the Association for Humanistic Gerontology, an international association intended to facilitate the emergence of positive and healthy images of aging and to develop programs for older people, and is former Director of the SAGE Project, the highly acclaimed holistic-health center for elders that originated in Berkeley, California. In addition to lecturing and conducting seminars nationwide on bodymind fitness, holistic health, aging, and human potential, he serves as a consultant to industry and government, and is an adjunct instructor in psychology, gerontology, and health-related sciences at several universities. He is the author of Bodymind *(1977),* Human Potential: Glimpses Into the Twenty-First Century *(with Dr. A. Villolodo, Tarcher/St. Martin's, 1980),* Lifelong Health and Well-Being *(forthcoming), and numerous articles on aging, health, fitness, and bodymind development.*

In this article, Dr. Dychtwald discusses the myths of aging, and some innovative programs that are reaching out to people over 60 to prove that the second half of life can be a growing and rewarding experience.

OUR SOCIETY IS, quite literally, "growing up." From being a culture of young people, we are rapidly shifting to being one in which people over fifty make up the fastest-growing segment of our population. In fact, if current trends continue, we can expect that by the end of the twentieth century more than half of all Americans will be more than fifty years old. In contrast, at the beginning of this century, the average American lived to be only 47 years old. The average life expectancy now stands at 74 years, and if current medical and environmental developments continue, it is not unreasonable to expect that many of us will live to be more than a century old. Although most people aren't aware of the incredible changes taking place in American demography, there is no way to avoid the fact that we are rapidly becoming a culture of adults and elders. Reflecting this shift, a great deal of social, political, and educational attention is now being directed away from the concerns of youth and toward the needs and potentials of America's 50,000,000 adults and elders.

Agism: Negative Concepts of the Elderly

Historically, the over-fifty American population have felt themselves to be a dead-end population group. Since most people didn't expect to live past the age of fifty or sixty, few took a serious interest in their later years, and fewer still effectively planned and prepared for the second half of their lives. Consistent with this lack of interest in aging and the adult years, few medical or counseling schools concern themselves with the physical, mental, or emotional needs of the over-fifty population. As a result, most health professionals *and* consumers throughout America simply choose not to think about getting older. Similarly, when people find themselves growing into their later years, there is an unrealistic attempt to disidentify with the aging process, and a tendency to yearn unsuccessfully for the pleasures of youth.

Let me cite an example. Several years ago I was producing a documentary about health, life design, and aging. During our initial filming, we decided to question people on the street about aging. We asked hundreds of people, "How old do you want to be before you die?" Generally, women aspired to more years than men, and the older people questioned wished for the longest

Ken
Dychtwald

Sandy Solomon

lifespans of all. But to our surprise and dismay, most people said they wished to life to be only 60 or 65 years old; very few people said that they wished to live longer. Many answered that they couldn't see any reason to live longer than 60, because after that there wouldn't be much fun, sex, good jobs, meaning, or independence. Since they believed (falsely) that, as they grew older, the things they identified now as important for good living would be fewer or gone, and would not be replaced by worthwhile alternatives, they had decided internally that their later years were bound to be a gloomy, unhappy time. Try as they would, few of these people could paint a rosy picture of their later years. In fact, many people said outright that they would prefer to die rather than live in such a diminished fashion.

Concern and fear about growing older is by no means a new phenomenon. In fact, we can look back to Greek mythology for an image that perfectly captures many of our current beliefs about aging: the tale of Eos. Eos, the beautiful daughter of the Titans Thea and Hyperion, was the goddess of dawn and the lover of all that was fresh and young. After falling in love with the handsome Trojan Tithonus, she carried him off to the gods, where she pleaded with Zeus to grant him immortality; unfortunately, she did not also ask that he be given eternal youth. Zeus granted her request, and as the years passed Tithonus grew older and older, his body growing more and more withered and decayed. Eventually, Eos became so disgusted by the sight of his infirmity that she locked Tithonus away in a chamber, where, it was said, he eventually turned into a chirping grasshopper.

Until recently, of course, few people have had to be concerned for very long about growing older without being healthy. And since most died before old age anyway, it was not entirely unreasonable to be unhappy about the passing of youth. As more people live to advanced ages, however, the issues and potentials inherent in the natural aging process are becoming more visible, more accepted, and more completely understood. And as aging continues to come out of the closet, we can expect that during the next few years there will be several large-scale social shifts related to aging and old age.

First, as more people realize that they will personally have an opportunity to grow older, they will try to uncover and redesign many of the cultural images of and beliefs about aging. Our culture now emphasizes youthful vigor, economic productiveness, and sexual and social competition, and older people are frequently pushed aside, demeaned, and denied a dignified and meaningful role in society. However, as large numbers of Americans become a part of the over-50 population, this situation will change dramatically. Although we may find this difficult to imagine now, we will soon feel it an honor and a privilege to be "aged," just as for years it has been a source of comfort and pride to be "young." Correspondingly, all the institutions that exist to support the psychological, social, political, educational, health, and spiritual needs of our culture will be forced to shift their focus away from a narrow youth orientation and toward one in which the entire age spectrum is respected, considered, and nourished appropriately.

Second, since most people would love to live a long and full life if they could also have their health and well-being, we can expect that a great deal of attention will soon be focused on preventing, avoiding, and dissolving the sources and causes of most age-related diseases. Such prevention will not be as hard as it sounds. In contrast to the turn of the century, when the primary killers were infectious diseases, infant mortality, and natural disasters, we now live in an era where the greatest contributors to disease and premature aging are stress, unhealthy lifestyles, lack of exercise, and poor nutrition. Since these are all factors over which individuals can exercise an enormous amount of control, I feel certain that in the near future there will be a massive movement toward adult and elder health, fitness, and creative life-design.

Although many people are beginning to examine the myths and realities of aging, our cultural and personal beliefs and feelings about aging and old age generally lack images of the old that are healthy, socially affirming, and dignified. Instead, old age is often viewed as a lifestage somehow separate from the rest of one's life: a time of decreased social worth and dependency; a time of physical decline and accompanying loss of beauty and health.

With these negative images so prevalent in the media, the arts, and the various economic and social institutions of our culture, it is no wonder that the aging process is viewed by many as a never-ending battle against the forces of loss, anxiety, dependency, loneliness, and sickness rather than as a time for personal growth, health, and significant social contribution. Similarly, since some aspects of the aging process are inevitable, many people wrongly believe that they have *no* control over the state of their bodies and minds or over their unique process of aging. Given this passive attitude, it is not surprising that many people do more to encourage their physical and mental deterioration than to prevent it!

Why is it that people have so many negative images of aging? And where do these images come from? How do cultural attitudes toward aging affect us personally? There are no simple answers to these questions, for every aspect of our lives contributes to these images. In many ways, however, aging is a shared experience, and the images of aging that fill and order our minds and bodies are largely drawn from a common cultural mythology of beliefs, expectations, and priorities.

Breakdown of Traditional Family and Social Roles

Historically, images about aging have been gained through direct personal experience with older people. Until recently people lived in, or at least in terms of, the extended family, so that each person had ample opportunity to interact with his or her grandparents, aunts, and uncles, and with the older relatives of friends and neighbors. The old community members, having been around the longest, were often well-known and usually knew the most about the various processes and procedures of life. However, recent changes in familial and social patterns have radically changed this format. People get married later, and thus some children never get to meet their grandparents. Many young people move away from home to attend college, to get married, and to work, and thus disengage themselves from active involvement in the lives of their parents and grandparents. Finally, with the advent of retirement communities, many older people choose to isolate themselves from young people; similarly, younger middle-aged people select appropriate age ghettos in which to live. Mandatory retirement, assembly-line factories, and massive stores and businesses have also eliminated the small shops, working teams, and apprenticeship models that provided a great deal of intergenerational involvement.

I have seen many of these social shifts in my own life. When I was young, my family lived in the same house as my grandparents, and as a result we were able to form close and loving relationships. I'm certain that when my grandparents cared for my brother and me as small children, they did so with the natural expectation that, when they were too old to be completely independent, we would exchange the favor and look out for them. I doubt they foresaw that times would change, and that some of the grandchildren—including myself—would move away. Now, even though I love my grandmother enormously and visit with her as often as I can, it is hard for me to be responsive to her daily needs from a distance of 3,000 miles. I suppose that some of the disappointment she may experience is not unlike what someone might feel if they worked for a company for forty-nine years, expecting to receive a lifetime retirement pension upon completion of the fiftieth year; only to have the company, six months before this date, decide to change its rules and do away with all retirement pensions. Certainly my grandmother is not unique in this predicament.

I also think that my parents would prefer to be more directly involved in my life and have me be more a part of their ongoing activities. Although we still visit with each other five or six times a year and speak to each other over the phone two or three times a week, I can sense their disappointment that I didn't stay close to home and participate in the family business. In particular, I think that my parents would like to be more influential in my decision-making processes, because they grew up identifying this as a normal part of their parental roles. Now, not only is this hard because I live so far away, but it is additionally difficult because with my training in psychology I'm hard-pressed to accept advice from anyone, let alone my parents. We have an additional laugh in our family because, since I specialize in aging, I also think I know what's best for them!

Such unexpected lifestyle changes as well as the imbalance between natural experience and formal education among the generations have all served to disrupt the traditional social mechanisms for mixed-aged interaction. As a result, many people find themselves in situations where there is no occasion for direct personal involvement with adults and elders; if there is interaction, the roles are often strained and undefined, making the interface awkward at best.

With this growing absence of meaningful personal exposure to life's second half, many young people find themselves in positions in which all of their beliefs and images about aging come to them secondhand or through the media. Yet, secondhand sources are notoriously inaccurate, and most of the media disregard the older population, focusing primarily on the thoughts, concerns, and pursuits of people under the age of fifty. In magazines and newspapers, and most especially on television, the experience of adults and elders is distorted and discounted, if represented at all. Advertisements seldom portray older people in a positive light, especially if the product relates to beauty, romance, or sexuality.

And strangely, many of the magazines and shows especially designed for people over 50 use young people in their advertisements and commercials. The powerful message that is being communicated to all of us each day is that older people are not worth writing about—nor are they interesting, beautiful, or sexy, nor do they deserve to have products created especially for them.

When adults and elders watch these shows and read these books and articles, they can not help feeling left out and worthless. The message comes through clearly: You have to be young to be okay. If aging got "better press," if advanced years meant maturity or inspired pride, telling an elder that he or she looked "young" (rather than, for example, beautiful or healthy) would be as insulting as telling a black person that he or she looked white.

In addition, we cannot measure how much these negative images of aging affect minds of young people, who haven't the experience to realize which messages are being left out of the media. Deprived of positive images, they tend to have a very limited perspective on the aging process. Recently I was struck by an interaction during a TV show on aging. The young interviewer, questioning a 93-year-old Kansas man about his life and work, asked, "Did you live in Topeka all of your life?" The elder gave him a bothered look, and answered, "Not yet!"

Discrimination by Architecture

The impact of these cultural priorities on the self-image and well-being of the aged does not stop with psychological abuse. These same negative and insensitive beliefs also affect the physical world, through the plans of architects, designers, and city developers. Most environments seem tailored to people with a standard body size and a specific range of mental and neurological performance levels. Our contemporary cities are like monstrous cookie cutters: they have been shaped to exclude people who cannot function within the constraints of these cities' design. Many older people cannot ride buses because the steps are too high; they cannot attend public events, because the transportation is inappropriate, walkways are too slippery, rooms are too dark, the lettering on the signs is too small, there are no elevators, and the bathrooms are hazardous. When one tries to perceive the world through the mind and body of an older person, it becomes immediately obvious that, as one ages, environments that were once comfortable and supportive become transformed into scarcely navigable obstacle courses. We see fewer and fewer adults and elder people around town because we have built our towns to exclude them, just as mandatory retirement, for example, excludes the over-65 population from the work force. Couple these factors with the rise in crime and violence, and we begin to see a frightening picture indeed for the older person who is still trying to function as a vital member of the community. Another sad point is that not enough older people realize that they and we have collectively created a world into which they are not meant to fit. Instead, they pick up and internalize the negative messages, and therefore, where outrage would be the appropriate response, too often we see resignation, low self-esteem, and anomie. In turn, these negative feelings become translated into physical and mental decline and sickness, thus enhancing the vicious cycle of agism.

As architects of our own immediate and distant futures, it is *our* responsibility to explore creative ways to generate positive and healthy images of aging and full life development. This point was brought home to me vividly during a seminar on life design that I recently conducted at a local medical school. An elderly woman seated in the back of the room asked if she might make a point to the class. She stood up and stated that she was 78 years old, and that when she was as young as we were, she had been very active in the social and political issues of her time. She explained that when she was in her twenties, there was a great feeling of excitement and vision in America and, correspondingly, an enormous effort to "improve the world" and to facilitate healthy and happy lifestyles for everyone. In many ways the vision and dreams of her generation have been realized, though it took fifty years and two generations for the seeds they planted to take root and blossom. Now, however, she noted with sadness that there was something that she and her young friends had neglected to consider when they were designing their "new age": they had left out the elderly! Now that she had arrived at "old age," she unhappily realized that she had helped to shape a world in which she does not fit.

As more is learned about healthy aging, it becomes increasingly clear that with the right attitude, preparation, and meaningful involvement, aging can be experienced as a thoroughly rewarding maturation process, not unlike the ripening of a fine wine or musical instrument. Indeed, in India it is believed that life begins at age 53, and that the years prior are just preparation! When the mind and body are healthy and vital, the second half of life may provide the ideal opportunity to cultivate joy and pleasure, develop self-awareness, begin and enjoy new skills and interests, and expand and deepen friendships.

At present, however, most medical, counseling, education, and leisure activities for adults are not designed to elicit health, joy, and vitality, but instead either deal primarily with problem-oriented treatment such as for drug dependency, or provide mindless entertainment and "pass-time" activities. This form of clinical and social approach does little to enrich the lives of the elderly, or to lessen the negative and deteriorating influences of stressful and unfulfilling lifestyles.

SAGE

In recent years, however, the growing national trend toward health promotion, personal growth, and self-improvement has begun to find its way into the world of the over-50 population. Encouraged by the revolution in physical fitness and human potential research, and by the rapidly growing field of holistic health, and discouraged by the rising costs of an ineffective health-care system, large numbers of people have begun to assume more positive responsibility for their health, well-being, and aging.

For example, the SAGE Project (Senior Actualization and Growth Explorations) which I co-directed for five years, is considered unique, partly because is is one of the few highly successful holistic-health programs in the world, and partly because we incorporated a variety of techniques from the personal-growth, human-potential, and preventive-health fields into our work with older people. These techniques include things like meditation, yoga, biofeedback, dance and art therapy, encounter, and journal writing. Most of these methods and processes are geared toward healing and growth, and had primarily been used with younger people, probably because of the fallacious assumption that only younger people can heal or grow or become more creative. We used these practices with people from sixty to ninety, even a hundred years old. We discovered, of course, that older people can definitely change their muscle tissue; they can grow intellectually and emotionally; they can develop new styles of living; they can become artistic in ways that perhaps they have never been before; they can literally begin to self-actualize perhaps more fully than any other age group.

Most activities for elders are based on the mistaken notion that reaching a certain age, perhaps 45 or 50, marks the point of physical and psychological decline. Consequently many professionals working with older people feel that their job is one of "maintenance." That is, they are doing their job well if the people don't get worse. The attitude at SAGE is that maintenance is not enough. Maybe it is necessary, but I know that I certainly don't want to be just "maintained" for half my life. The SAGE approach attempts to go far past the notion of health care as maintenance, and instead seeks to discover and design activities, programs, and relationships for elders that generate those feelings of joy, pleasure, integrity, creativity, love, confidence, and health that we all like to feel. SAGE involves its participants with very dynamic, exciting, experiential programs, and the results have been quite astonishing. We have noticed that older people have just as much potential for change and self-development as younger people. For example, according to one SAGE participant, 77-year-old Herb Pillars:

> "I came here afraid of dying, and even more afraid of being a burden in my old age. Now I'm not nearly so afraid . . . . As for the changes, I came here with arthritis in my hands, terrible backaches, and a stiff neck. I still have a little trouble with the arthritis, but the backache is gone, and I can now twist my head and see the traffic behind me on the road when I'm driving. Also, I used to smoke. You can't smoke and deep breathe at the same time!"

Another SAGE member, 70-year-old Frances Burch, states:

"I've seen people in this group change their physical and mental outlook. They're more open and responsive, their lives are more exciting, and they have more possibilities and choices. I feel much better myself. I've seen things go on here that are amazing . . . self-healing. Here we're learning to tap new personal power sources through our spiritual growth. I'm finding energy that I haven't had in years."

When SAGE began in January 1974, we knew of few people who were attempting to incorporate personal growth and holistic-health methods and beliefs into their work with older people. Those who were experimenting with humanistically focused health, education, and recreation methods were doing so alone, usually with very little financial or psychological support, and with minimal contact with others throughout the country who were involved with similar activities.

However, through outreach, training, and national development programs, we discovered that there are thousands of people and institutions committed to many of the same innovative visions and practices. Although there had been a growing body of people and information that support a humanistic approach to gerontological services, programs, and research, there wasn't a formal organization or network established to act as a clearing-house and central resource agency for all of the shared ideas, techniques, materials, and experiences. As a result, many people and projects lacked support, stimulation, and relevant information-sharing.

The A.H.G.

In response to this situation, the Association for Humanistic Gerontology was created in September 1977. I initially designed A.H.G. to serve simultaneously as a professional association, an international resource-sharing network, and a conference-producing and training organization. In its short period of operation, A.H.G. has already attracted members from throughout the United States, Canada, South America, and Europe.

The basic premise of "humanistic gerontology" is that aging can be a full and thoroughly rewarding growth and maturation process, that the later years can bring a unique freedom to learn, explore, and share, unburdened by the intense social and economic competition, child-rearing responsibilities, and worrisome jobs that frequently absorb enormous amounts of time in the earlier years of life. Inherent in this "humanistic" approach to health care is a deep appreciation for the unity of mind, body, and spirit, a strong emphasis on preventive education and self-responsibility, and the belief that growth, exercise, good nutrition, and meaningful interpersonal involvement are necessary ingredients of any healthy lifestyle.

In recent years, interest in preventive and holistic-health methods seems to be reaching nearly revolutionary proportions, as countless mental and physical gerontological health-care providers nationwide have begun to use these new approaches in a variety of formats and settings. Successful programs of this type include senior exercise classes, foster-grandparent programs, oral-history projects, elderhostels, emeritus college programs, health-maintenance classes, senior-center activities, intergenerational communes and communities, involvement in the creative arts, such as music, dancing, and painting, peer discussion groups, co-counseling, journal writing, advocacy groups, public lectures and events, activities at Y's and churches, and effective media such as the "Over Easy" television show.

Reflecting the need for treating the "whole person," there has also been a reemergence of interest in health-team-oriented clinics and cross-modality referral services, in which physical-health and mental-health professionals and lay professionals join to share and blend their skills and resources.

Certainly no one method or technique will effectively remedy all the problems of our older population; yet it becomes increasingly urgent that, just as lifestyles, healthstyles, and aging patterns have changed in the past few decades, so must the helping professions change to become more directly relevant to the unique needs and potentials of our continually expanding elder population. If the trend toward disease prevention, health promotion, personal growth, and self-responsibility continues, it will be increasingly appropriate to focus time, energy, and money on activities, programs, and methodologies that support a humanistically styled, holistic approach to mental and physical health for elders.

Identifying and uprooting the agism and negativity that pervade our culture, our bodies, and our minds will be a delicate and arduous task, but it is a crucial one. As we move collectively toward the twenty-first century, there is no choice but to liberate aging from the sickness, despair, and premature death within which it has historically been encased. And, if there is to be a healthy, fit, and joyous adult population alive in America, it is essential that we all take responsibility *now* for initiating the kinds of personal, cultural, and planetary practices and priorities that will transform our images of aging, and give us compassion, strength, health, awareness, and creativity throughout our lives.

For further information about the activities of the Association for Humanistic Gerontology, contact the A.H.G. offices at 1711 Solano Avenue, Berkeley, CA 94707, (415) 525-3128.

13 HELPING THE DYING PERSON
Charles Garfield, Ph.D.

Terminal illness has a profound effect on the patient, his family, and the health practitioners who work with him. In counseling those who are aware they are dying, the skill of a practitioner or someone trained in the process of dying can be invaluable to the patient and those close to him.

Dr. Charles A. Garfield received his Ph.D. in clinical psychology from the University of California at Berkeley. He is a lecturer and author, Clinical Professor of Medical Psychology at the Cancer Research Center in San Francisco, and founder and director of a unique service, the Shanti Project, a volunteer counseling program for patients and families facing life-threatening illnesses.

Among his many books, Dr. Garfield has written Rediscovery of the Body, *and* Stress and Survival. *He is editor of* Psychosocial Care of the Dying Patient.

THE MAIN STIMULUS for my interest in working with dying people was an experience I had during my internship. I was in the last year of my Ph.D. program in clinical psychology and was working with a twenty-year-old man who was dying of leukemia. I learned more about what compassion and caring and counseling are really about in the six weeks that I spent with Luis than I had in my previous four years in graduate school. My interest in the helping professions stemmed from the hope that caring, helping, and compassion were to be the main elements. What I learned in graduate school was that intellectual activity and analysis seemed to be the main elements.

Now, for the very first time in all those years in a heavyweight Ph.D. program, I was doing the kind of helping that I thought I would be doing when I first entered the program. It was my first realization of the time-limited nature of working with dying people. The immediacy of death and the limitations of available time allowed things to happen between two people that aren't usually possible in normal social intercourse. It was very moving, and very powerful.

Dealing with death is important because it can lend a sense of immediacy to daily life. When we realize that death is always to our left—in Castaneda's terms—that we don't have all the time in the world, then we understand how each act might be our last.

On the other hand, one of the most boring things I can imagine is endless philosophizing about dying and death. I hear a lot of people talking about blissful deaths and death-acceptance, and I wonder whether they are really talking about their wives, their lovers, their mothers, themselves. I've worked with over three hundred people who have died; many of them became my friends. If I've learned anything from those experiences, it's that working with people who are dying, going through the loss each time, experiencing the separation, lends a much different character to your life than philosophizing about dying or talking about death in the abstract. That's why I have very little tolerance for cocktail-party chatter about dying. The closer death moves to your inner circle of special people, the people who are the most precious in the world to you, then the more powerful the fact of dying becomes, and the more it throws you back on your own personal resources. It forces you to confront the basic, existential questions: what is your life anyway? What is the purpose of it? What is the meaning of the universe in general? Questions about God and one's own spirituality become really urgent.

When you're working with people who are dying, these questions are no longer just topics for a stimulating conversation on a Saturday afternoon. When you're sitting with a man who's dying of acute leukemia and who has six weeks left to live, the issue of continuity of existence after death is obviously urgent for him. When we're faced with the doctor telling us that we have six weeks to live, we learn what's important and what isn't very quickly. Never have I heard anyone say that the most important thing in his life was his Mercedes. People always talk about relationships, about what things they have accomplished that they

*Charles
Garfield*

Karen Preuss

think were worthwhile. It sets a clear priority on what kinds of things we should spend our time on.

In some cultures, death is a cause for celebration; in our culture it's a time for sadness and bereavement. There are several reasons why we look at death differently from some other cultures. First, even in those cultures that currently have a sense of celebration about death, there is still the paradox of the difference between the severing of the personal connection, which we respond to with loss and grieving and sadness, and the conviction that there's a greater cosmological system in which we all have a part and which allows for a strong sense of transformation rather than termination. Even in those cultures that we would think most likely to celebrate a death, such as traditional Japanese or Indian culture, there's still a sense of personal termination and loss. However, it's coupled with a sense of celebration and transformation because the person is moving into a different realm; there's a strong conviction among the survivors that such a movement is taking place. In post-industrial, twentieth-century America, the general feeling is that the death of a loved one is an abrupt ripoff, a final termination of the relationship. We don't seem to have the other half of that paradox to fall back on, except intellectually. By and large, the loss of the person you care about most in the world is still experienced as a powerful, abrupt, painful termination. Apparently most of us don't have a strong-enough belief in transformation, in other realms of existence, or in the notion of a cosmic order to be comforted by these notions. Our philosophy is like a little pebble in a giant ocean of emotionality.

In other cultures, both the personal and the "cosmic" frames of reference seem to lend more strength, especially since both are more powerfully based on a religious or spiritual system. We could boil much of the pragmatics of Eastern and Western religions down to the same few working principles that many of the dying people whom I have known intimately arrived at for evaluating their own lives. When these people talk about what matters most, they talk about meaning, altruism, and compassion as being of ultimate importance. The one thing that stands out most is the amount of love that a person gives during a lifetime, the amount of caring, the amount of goodness. When you hear such insights coming from a 55-year-old truck driver who's dying of lung cancer, or from an 83-year old farmer from northern California, or from other folks whom one would not normally expect to have those kinds of reflections and sentiments, it is a deeply moving experience.

It's not surprising that we see the grim reaper as the contemporary mythic figure for death in post-industrial America. In other cultures it might be an entirely different figure. Most Americans walk around much of the time without a strong sense of being related to the absolute, to what Aldous Huxley called "the basic allrightness of the universe." Here in the San Francisco Bay Area we like to take credit for all sorts of avant-garde things. In reality, many of the avant-garde folks I know walk around with the same sets of feelings as the people from Jersey City or Des Moines. For most of us that sense of being in touch with cosmic processes is still only at kindergarten level. In the face of imminent death, it's often very little in the way of support.

Many of us still fear death as the end. We experience a "How could I not be among you" syndrome. Indeed, how could I not be any more? It feels like the end of the time line. You walk your time line; and off into the abyss; boom! you're dead! That's what the existentialists talk about. Now, if this time here is all you have, and you feel you haven't made the right use of it then the end of that time line poses quite a threat. Cessation of existence is a scary prospect.

Suppose, in contrast, that you are a Hindu sitting in the streets of Benares begging, and that you face the prospect of dying. In your cosmology there are many other lifetimes. You have an emotional conviction more than an intellectual construction. You are quite positive that there are many other lifetimes, that things will be different later.

"Master," asked the student, "what is it like at death?"

"Why ask me?"

"Because you're a Zen master."

"Yes, but not a dead one."

I think the main reason that death assumes the character of the grim reaper to so many people in our society has less to do with how one faces death than with how one lives life. Facing death seems to be a corollary of facing life. We might say that "deathstyles" seem to be very, very similar to lifestyles, the means a person uses to cope with the vicissitudes of life. People who can face death without a sense of abject terror are, in my experience, those people who have lived their lives from a basically strong cosmological or religious base. They seem to have a sense of the basic "allrightness" of the universe. On the other hand, there are a great many people who feel that facing one's death tranquilly is absolutely not appropriate. Remember Dylan Thomas raging at the dying of the light.

We need to know more about how to support people who are dying and what the dying process is like. The available literature is sometimes not very helpful. It's like reading a book on how to ride a bicycle. You can learn some things about riding a bicycle from a book, but not nearly as much as from trying to ride a bicycle and falling off a few times. You learn much more from one deeply experienced situation working with a dying person than you would from reading the entire research literature. It seems nearly impossible to capture the flavor of the experience in a book. It's like attempting to describe orgasm in words. I doubt that anybody could write a book about orgasm which could make me feel the way I do when I'm having an orgasm. I doubt even more strongly that somebody could write a book about what it really feels like to be in extended contact with somebody who is dying that would capture the flavor of it accurately.

When I'm introduced to the patient, I'm not called a "death counselor" or introduced as a psychologist for the dying. I discarded the exorcist model a long time ago. Sneaking in the door at the last minute to exorcise the demons is not an acceptable style for me. Invading the deathbed environment without a history of relationship is like walking into the middle of a sexual intimacy. Consequently, my role is defined in a more formal sense as that of a psychologist whose responsibility is to see those people with cancer and other life-threatening illnesses who are having emotional problems. Naturally, that includes just about every cancer patient. A patient in a teaching hospital experiences a constant sea of faces coming to the bedside. Although it's good to get lots of opinions and expertise, it is extremely demanding for the patient to keep repeating procedures. I'm just one more doctor who comes in, one whose role is to take care of those emotional needs that are not attended to by the other people. If the patient tells me that things are going well, that he doesn't need anybody to talk to, that's fine. I leave my phone number and let him know how to get in touch with me in case anything comes up. Then I make a graceful exit.

Some people will read my badge and see "staff psychologist." There are still lots of old superstitions and taboos against talking to a psychologist. Later on, sometimes weeks or even months later, I'll get a request from a nurse: "You remember that patient down the hall? He asked about you the other day. He wanted to know if you could come in and talk." Usually some crisis has occurred. Now the impact of the illness has begun to take its toll. Now there is fear, and no place to get answers.

Working in the hospital, I am often in the role of patient advocate rather than staff psychologist. I'm the person who comes to the bedside without a strictly medical agenda. I'm the one who sits with the person specifically to listen. Sometimes I experience myself as a secretary at the bedside of the boss who tells me what things I can do to help. I do everything I can and report back. Sometimes it's "I haven't seen my physician in a couple of days, and I need to ask him some questions. Can you get hold of him?"

Sometimes it's information that the nursing staff can handle. Sometimes it's making a phone call to the family. It's a role that could be filled by many people in the hospital, but it's better filled by somebody who has some influence, who can make things happen. Many of the activities could be performed by volunteers, like those in the Shanti Project.

Sensitivity to the spiritual aspects of being is needed when death is imminent. Almost everyone I've worked with has faced the basic existential questions: What is the meaning of life? Is there anything after death? Purpose and meaning become extremely important issues. Such confrontation requires the companion or counselor, the mental-health professional, the physician, the nurse—anyone in contact with someone who is going through such questioning—to face their own fears. The ultimate terror for many people is to engage in that sort of questioning alone. Did my life have any meaning? Did I make a mistake? Did I blow the whole thing? Frequently, the conversation is one-sided. Nobody is willing to take up the other half of the dialogue. Playing such a role forces self-reflection in a very challenging way.

Such discussions have made clear to me the distinction between belief and knowledge. I may believe something to be true, but if that belief is anything short of an iron-clad conviction, facing my death will make a shambles of it. My experience is that those people who approach death without a strong sense, integrated both emotionally and intellectually, of their basic relatedness to universal processes may find themselves in dire straits. Those people who've had a deep, life-long conviction, or who perhaps experience conversion on the deathbed, manage to die in a way that feels like it's "in synch" with a strong spiritual process. I'm acutely aware that I live in a geographical area where there's much talk about life after death, paranormal experience, and reincarnation. Exploring these notions is extremely important and exciting. However, if one buys in too quickly, assuming as knowledge what really is belief, and not too strong a belief at that, then one can be sure that acute leukemia will make a shambles of all those little books on reincarnation that you have at your bedside.

On the other hand are the so-called nonbelievers. Supposedly they have no beliefs to be shattered. The problem is that "no belief" is also a belief, one that tends to get questioned quickly. It's fascinating how people who have had no strong religious affiliation will start asking what I think about God and the afterlife. Suddenly, they start actively engaging those issues they once discarded as "merely" philosophical concepts. On the deathbed the issue of life after death is not comfortable social talk, but has a real urgency.

I have worked with some people who faced death existentially and who felt okay about it. These people had a self-generated definition of purpose and meaning in life that was as clear as any I've ever encountered. They seemed to have done what they came to do in very concrete terms. They had a sense of completion, a sense of having accomplished a mission. Consequently, death to them made all the sense in the world. Several were women who defined their roles in a clear, traditional fashion. I remember a 75-year-old woman who told me that she came into the world to bear children, to be a good wife and a good mother, making sure that her children grew up in fine fashion. Once her job was finished, she had no interest in contemplating the philosophical and intellectual issues of an afterlife. She had done what she came to do; her job was finished; and that was it.

The men I have cared for tended to encounter more difficulties. It wasn't as easy for them to know they'd done it right. Male children are raised to think that they always have to be in control of the situation. Facing death really brings up the fear of loss of control. The hardest hit are those individuals who have experienced themselves in terms of what I call "the fastest gun in the west" model: people who had the illusion of maximum control. An example is the corporate businessman who experiences himself as being in control of his whole universe. Suddenly, he finds himself at 61 on a bed somewhere in a hospital because of a heart attack. He is totally out of control, in as fearfully difficult situation as he's likely to encounter. He usually confronts all sorts of terrors, coping with the fear of death and the threat of dying.

This is not to say that women face death more tranquilly than men. The form of coping is simply different. Teaching people to take responsibility for as much of their lives as they possibly can, to experience themselves as effective agents in the world, is important, but it also has its limits. When we push that philosophy past reasonable boundaries, we wind up with all these Wyatt Earps running around trying to shoot it out at high noon against the Grim Reaper. We should remember that survival—both physical and emotional—is a collective act. Precious few of us, whether dying or fighting to avoid death, ever manage to deal honestly with these events all by ourselves. We all need help.

5 SPIRITUAL AWARENESS AND HEALING

WHAT IS SPIRITUAL AWARENESS? If asked, each of us would respond to this question from a subjective point of view. It is likely that no person's experience of spiritual awareness is the same as another's.

Spiritual awareness and healing have been a universal mystery. There is no doubt that healing has occurred by the "laying on" of hands, the power of prayer, within meditation, by some subjective experience. But we are still struggling to understand what does happen within the body/mind/spirit to effect spiritual cures of disease and handicaps of the body and mind.

Most often we hear from those who study spiritual healing that internal and external environment plays an important part. The setting, the circumstances, the personal background of the healer and healee, the inclinations of those who play a part, are all meaningful. Perhaps the most important point to recognize is that the spiritual aspects of oneself can play a significant role in healing.

This section, then, deals with the healer, being healed, and the effects of spiritual awareness on health.

Dr. Bloomfield's article, "Discovering the Spiritual Dimensions of Medicine," discusses spiritual awakening and health.

Spiritual healer Olga Worrall, born with the gifts of healing and clairvoyance, talks about her beliefs and her insights and feelings gained from more than 25 years of experience in healing.

Ruth Carter Stapleton was transformed and reborn and with her release from personal distress, she gained the gift of promoting inner healing in others. Her article is the story of her ministry, of how she changed from an unhappy human being to a healer of others. It is fitting that we end this book with her article on the importance of the spirit, the hope of joy, and the power of love.

A.P.K.

14 DISCOVERING THE SPIRITUAL DIMENSIONS OF MEDICINE

Harold H. Bloomfield, M.D.

In this article, Dr. Bloomfield discusses his personal discovery of the spiritual dimensions of medicine. From his awakening to the effects of TM on his health and well-being, Dr. Bloomfield came to see spirituality as an important part of health and an essential factor in healing.

ALL THROUGH MY MEDICAL TRAINING, I had no courses on stress or stress reduction. (I have since become very friendly with Hans Selye, but I didn't learn about his work while I was going through medical school.) We had no courses on physical fitness, or on nutrition; there was a little bit touching on it in biochemistry, but that was just the Krebs Cycle and what a carbohydrate looks like chemically, not practical nutrition. There were no courses on sex education, or on the spirit, or on death and dying. And it was only ten years ago that I completed my medical training! I did have the feeling that there was something missing. Indeed, I went to Yale for training in psychiatry as part of my own search for the "psyche-iatrous," that which can heal the spirit and the mind. I am sure I was looking for my own fulfillment in that process, hoping I could then pass something on to others. I found that most of the people who were training me were good people, but really were no more mentally healthy, no more an embodiment of the highest potentials of the human spirit, than an average group of civil-service workers would have been. They didn't have the magic keys to the full development of one's human potential.

My first entry into holistic health began with T-groups, that is, encounter groups. I got a tremendous amount out of seeing how other people were viewing me. I started to see in my personal life that there was sometimes a discrepancy between what I was feeling and what I was putting out to the world. As I started to recognize some of that incongruity, I realized this had applications to psychiatry. From that point on, I think, I became more interested in dealing with my patients in a real way than in terms of how I thought a psychiatrist should behave with a patient. That was a very important transition point for me. As I valued being more myuself, I became more myself with my patients, instead of trying to play the *role* of a psychoanalyst. I found that results were better with me being me, knowing that I was taking risks.

Another major change in me resulted from my getting involved with the Transcendental Meditation technique. I had not, up until that point, thought of myself as being a particularly stressed individual; but certainly, looking back, I and my colleagues were a lot more stressed than I had any idea of at the time. I have been meditating regularly now twice a day for well over six years, and I feel a great deal of gratitude for having been introduced to TM and making that a regular part of my life. It certainly facilitated my reducing my own stress level and getting in touch with more and more of my own feelings, my own creativity, who I am as a person.

Along with the encounter groups, the TM, I began more and more to follow my instincts. In other words, I would spend time with people that I genuinely liked and cared for. I also discovered that healthy cooking was much better for me than the processed, fast-foods stuff that had been my steady diet until then. As I began to meditate regularly, I lost my taste, quite literally, for fast foods. I could feel what they were doing to me. It was by pursuing such experiences that I rediscovered, at least for myself, the spiritual side of health, which had been all but lost from modern medicine. By the term spiritual, I mean having a sense of meaning, purpose, and direction in life. One can get that from some specific religious practice, perhaps the religion that one was brought up with, or from reading the great philosophers, or perhaps from serving some larger community purpose. What is important here is to identify with something larger than one's own individual ego, to begin participating in a larger societal or cosmic process that allows one to feel a sense of service or community. People who are spiritually healthy, who have the sense of meaning and purpose, are less likely to fall ill in the first place, and, if they do fall ill, are more likely to recover faster.

We are also recognizing the other side of the coin, that periodically people go through spiritual crises in their lives. These are a very important part of growth, and are not to be avoided. I think a lot of what we have been labeling "anxiety neurosis" and have been trying to medicate with Valium and Librium are really spiritual crises, which have to be dealt with in terms of spiritual values. These constitute a natural process, which we should allow to unfold, so that we can confront some of the deeper issues in our lives, such as whether we feel good about the kind of work we are doing, and whether the flow of our lives corresponds with our sense of values. We have to examine such things, not push them underground. In *The Holistic Way to Health and Happiness* I describe many people who were diagnosed as neurotics or as suffering from tension, but who were actually going through profound spiritual crises. Once they were able to recognize that the problem was not just a tension, anxiety, or low-grade depression to be medicated away, that, on the contrary, it was a call of their deeper self to integrate some basic values and inclinations into their larger stream of their lives, they underwent a profound awakening that led to much greater health, energy, and enthusiasm, and to some very important blossomings of their creativity.

15 SPIRITUAL THERAPY
Olga Worrall, Ph.D.

Olga Worrall was born in 1906 in Cleveland, Ohio. She has been practicing her "unconventional healing," as she calls it, since 1928, and has never accepted any payment for it. She is an ordained Christian minister, and has been a Director of the New Life Clinic at Baltimore's Mt. Washington Methodist Church since 1950. For many years with her husband, Ambrose Worrall, and now alone since his death in 1972, Dr. Worrall has given generously and freely of her time and gifts to those in need. She has been tested repeatedly in laboratory settings at UCLA, at Rosary Hill in Buffalo, New York, and at other universities.

Olga Worrall's model of "unconventional healing" emerges from a specific worldview. According to Dr. Worrall, her "healing" involves the channeling of energy into a healee. The energy comes from a "universal field of energy" which is common to all creation. It stems from God, the universal source of all intelligence and power.

Some healees experience Dr. Worrall's "laying on of hands" as an unusual degree of heat; others say they feel something akin to a small electric charge or shock.

Whatever her "gifts," however they work—and they do bring healing for many people—her story is one of the more remarkable among the New Healers.

Her biography, Olga Worrall: Mystic with the Healing Hands, *was written by Edwina Cerutti. Mrs. Worrall has co-authored three other books,* The Gift of Healing, Explore Your Psychic World, *and* Your Power to Heal, *all published by Harper and Row.*

134

WHEN I WAS THREE, my parents discovered that, of all their children, I had the unusual ability to see dead people. At the age of eight when I touched people, they said they felt better. But it wasn't until after I married my husband that I realized that there was such a thing as the psychic world. I just thought everybody experienced what I did.

My husband was a scientist and an engineer as well as a very gifted psychic, clairvoyant, and healer. We didn't meet as a result of these attributes; we met at a college party. It wasn't until after we were married that we began to discuss such things. We realized then that this was to be our ministry, our avocation, to help people.

My father was a theologian in the Russian-Greek Orthodox Church, which I was brought up in. My mother was a Hungarian countess and a Roman Catholic. My husband was a very staunch Methodist. In England his particular church was called the "Primitive Methodists."

It is Christian to believe in life after death, and in the power of spiritual healing. Jesus returned to demonstrate immortality. After he died on the cross, he came back to his followers and said, "Look, people, I live on. You can too." Also, the very foundation of the Christian church was the gifts of the Spirit. If we had not had the clairvoyant ability of our Lord Jesus, if we had not had his healing manifestations and his resurrection, there wouldn't be any Christianity.

About 300 years after the founding of the Christian church, the theologians took over. In theology, you are supposed to argue. Even today, they are so busy arguing that the Church is falling down over their heads and they don't realize it. They are too blind to know what the essence of the Christian teaching really is. Consequently, our young people are not being taught the mystical aspects of Christ's life and must go elsewhere to get them. I've studied other religions. As a Christian, I don't have to be a slave to various human-made gods, and I'm as free as can be, since I understand the spiritual laws that govern all persons, be they Christian or non-Christian.

This doesn't mean I have nothing to do with organized Christianity. I lecture to ministers in the so-called "established church." I've been a member of the Methodist Church since 1950, and have been conducting healing services in the church

*Olga
Worrall*

during this entire time. I never accept money for my healing
ministry, no love offerings, no salary. God gave me this gift, and
I'm sharing it.

I teach young doctors how to combine it with their traditional
techniques. I call it spiritual therapy. I also teach ministers how to
better understand the problems of their parishioners who may experience psychic phenomena. I feel this is something that should
be taught in all our seminaries, but unfortunately our seminarians
are not prepared for this kind of ministry. They are not taught
how to handle bereavement, and know practically nothing of the
art of healing. From what I have observed, I gather that our
seminaries concentrate on an exclusively materialistic intellectual teaching.

I've had many seminarians come to me ready to chuck
everything because they feel they don't know the true mystical
Christ. They don't know what spiritual healing means. They are
not being taught how to cope with the death experience. There

are books being written by doctors to tell the ministers something that the ministers should be telling the doctors: that there is a *continuity* to life.

Some of these young ministers, even old ministers, are frightened when they have to officiate at a funeral. They don't know what to say. They want to run away. Yet, if they were properly trained in seminary, they could be the greatest comfort the bereaved could have. The bereaved very often have to comfort the ministers.

I am a seer. I know that when death takes over the physical body, we step out of our physical bodies into the next dimension. There is a continuity of existence, another plane of consciousness. If I didn't really know this, I could not profess to be a Christian.

I see life after death as part of a progressive evolution of existence. I am not a reincarnationist. When I meet reincarnationists, I am struck by how they recycle famous historical figures. I think I've met about twenty Cleopatras, and I don't know how many Napoleons and John the Baptists. They think every illness is caused by *karma*, by misdeeds in a previous life, that is, by God punishing His children! How awful to even contemplate!

When I have learned all I can in this life, I'm going to go on to the next progressive dimension. I don't feel there is any retrogression in God's universe. There is constant forward movement. Who would want to come back here, anyway, when we can learn all that we have to learn in the next dimension?

No one knows what the ultimate is. These things are not revealed to us, because I'm sure we wouldn't know how to cope with them. The great mysteries of life would probably throw us for a loop if we knew all the answers. As we grow, we get a little bit here, and a little bit there, and that's how we continue to progress spiritually.

We are individualized sparks of God. This essence-spark is pure energy that comes from the source of all creation. We can call it what we will: "Law," "The Nameless One." I like to refer to this power as "God." Some don't like to use the word "God." We don't know what it is, but we know we are experiencing it. It is right there. We are feeling it. We are bathing in it. It is all around us.

If I knew what actually happens in the process of spiritual or unconventional healing, I would be fantastically rich. One technique I use in my ministry is the "laying on of hands." However, I also do "absent healing," which is healing at a distance, intercessory prayer for people who can't be with me. They phone or write, and give me their names, and I hold them in my prayers.

Laboratory experiments indicate that there is an energy that flows through me when I am in a state of doing healing. I maintain that a healer is so biologically constructed that he or she is a carrier for this energy. You can be a bad person, you can be a good person, you can have green eyes or brown eyes. When God distributes these gifts to his children, He seems not to take into account what our failings are. If we do discover that we have these abilities, it is our responsibility to spiritualize them, and keep them on a very high level.

It is not that you have to be a good person in order to be a carrier for this energy. That is how we get "black magic" and "white magic." Rasputin, for instance, started with a marvelous gift of healing, but tempted as he was by adulation, money, and power, he began to use it in the wrong way.

My husband called the healing energy "para-electricity," meaning above or beyond the electrical properties known on earth. A healer is so constructed biologically that he or she transforms this para-electricity into an energy that can be used by all living systems, man, animal, or plant.

There are instances when this energy is not effective. We can use the analogy of a battery. The healer acts as a channel for recharging the physical battery. You can recharge a battery only so many times. After a while the battery will no longer hold a charge. It is the same with our life energy. After a while the body no longer desires to hold the charge. The spirit wants to move on; the body is no longer tenable. The human being then enters another *phase* of life, but continues to live, and grow, and learn!

16 SPIRITUAL HEALING
Ruth Carter Stapleton

"Inner healing is a process of emotional reconstruction experienced under the guidance of the Holy Spirit." These words can best describe Ruth Carter Stapleton's healing ministry which began some years ago. Mrs. Stapleton came to her work after an emotional experience during a retreat in North Carolina. This experience interested her in the possibilities of faith healing. She returned to college, earned a degree at Methodist College in Fayetteville, and did postgraduate work in psychology at the University of North Carolina at Chapel Hill. Mrs. Stapleton is not ordained, nor is she a licensed psychologist. Her work, her ministry, has led her to all parts of the country and abroad. She lectures and conducts workshops for various groups within the church and at church-sponsored conferences, including ones on holistic health and healing and therapy groups. In addition, she is the author of two books, The Gift of Inner Healing, *and* The Experience of Inner Healing.*

Her work combines guided fantasy with Christian belief. Its purpose is to replace negative memories with "God-inspired reconstructions of those memories." Her guided fantasies take people back through time to the moment of conception, then bring the healing energy of Christ to the situation.

Mrs. Stapleton is the sister of President Jimmy Carter.

MY WORK IS CENTERED in Jesus Christ; He is the basis of everything I do. The process of healing involves moving into the unconscious with the unseen, spiritual, creative energy of the Holy Spirit. Other approaches to holistic healing don't seem to use any part of the Trinity energies. However, I see many other

Ruth
Carter
Stapleton

Christopher Wentworth

similarities, and I have learned a great deal from various aspects of holistic medicine, such as having a proper diet, using food supplements, getting enough exercise, and generally reconditioning one's habit-patterns into a healthy form of living. I appreciate the research in those areas; it has been very helpful to me.

My Discovery of Healing

I first came in touch with my own ability to facilitate healing about 17 years ago. It involved a member of my own family. About two weeks before this first healing experience happened, I had my first session with a group of people who were searching into a deeper dimension of the Spirit within. At that meeting there was a great transformation in my life. I became aware of the reality and validity of prayer. Prayer really did work for me. The experiences of that week were so intense that when I came home, I retreated into the country to be closer to nature, to be alone with my children, away from most people.

Back in town, a week or so later, I sent my son, Scotty, to the drugstore to do some shopping. He had been gone a little longer than usual, when suddenly my husband came running into the house and said, "There's been a terrible accident: Scotty has been hit by a car, and he's not expected to live! I've already talk-ed to the doctor; it's almost hopeless! Scotty was alert at first, but now he's regressing into a deeper coma." My husband returned to the hospital, and I left to get the babysitter. Driving the car, I could hardly see through the tears as I began screaming hysterically. Then I remembered what a psychologist had said at that retreat: we can move into a realm of consciousness where we begin to flow with the universe, where every experience becomes one of positive affirmation. We can express this affirmation by giving thanks for every experience that happens, whether it seems good or bad. This concept was totally new to me; such a thought had never before crossed my mind.

Driving along at that moment, I wanted to call that psychologist and get him to do this thing for my son, but I couldn't remember his name or address. So, in a moment of panic, I just screamed out in the car, "I thank God for the acci-dent; I thank God for every person involved; and I thank God for the good that is coming out of it."

I have had few so-called "mystical experiences" in my life. Although I am highly sensitive, I usually operate methodically, by means of concrete, well-tested theories. However, in that mo-ment a flowing sense of peace and allrightness about everything came upon me. I didn't feel that Scotty was necessarily going to live, nor did I feel that he was going to die. There was simply nothing but perfect peace, no matter what the results turned out to be.

Suddenly, I began to sing (I never sing; singing is certainly not joy for me), but I began to sing, "I have a joy, joy, joy in my heart." I sang compulsively; I couldn't stop. I still don't know why I did it. I had so much emotion; I guess I needed to ventilate. After I picked up the babysitter, I sang all the way back to the house.

At the hospital, everybody was in tears. Even the doctor was upset. Scotty lay there as though dead. I moved a bed into his room and got everybody to leave. Throughout the night I continued to experience this terrific internal rejoicing. I even went to sleep, although I woke up several times to check on him.

About 10 o'clock the next morning I heard him say, "Who are you?" I jumped up and saw his eyes were open. I said, "Your mother."

Then he asked, "Who am I?" and I said, "Your name is Scotty."

"What am I doing here?"

"You've been run over. You've been in an accident."

He was about 13 at the time, so the next thing he said was, "Oh, could you get me some funny books?" I flew out and called for the doctor and my family. Within an hour, he was back to a state of absolutely perfect consciousness.

The doctor said that never in the history of medical science had this particular type of concussion proven to be anything other than fatal. That experience was my first step in realizing that there is something unseen which we can work with to allow miraculous things to happen.

Shortly thereafter, I began to actually move into a ministry of physical healing. Many times I saw healings take place; and many times I saw nothing happen. But for about the next 10 years, I devoted myself almost exclusively to the healing of the body with prayer through Jesus Christ.

Sometimes people ask me if it's necessary to recognize Jesus Christ in order to experience a healing. I think the faith has to be somewhere. Many people come to me for healing through prayer who have no particular faith in Jesus, but they seem to have faith in my faith. Jesus was quoted as saying to parents that their faith had made their children well, and also saying directly to people, "Your faith has made you well."

A Weekend with Doctors

For many years, my work seemed to have no effect on the traditional practice of medicine. Traditionally, the two worlds of spiritual healing and modern medicine were like East and West:

"Never the twain shall meet." However, several years ago I was invited to be part of a team of three healers who met for three full days with 35 doctors who were very skeptical about the validity of spiritual healing. These doctors were getting sick and tired of hearing their patients say, "God healed me," after all kinds of therapy and medication seemed ineffective. At any rate, these 35 doctors were willing to take all day Friday, Saturday, and Sunday to prove to themselves once and for all it was not valid.

Starting with the sessions on Friday, the going was very rough. I was asked difficult questions I'd never faced before. I hit quite a few deadends. By Saturday, I was beginning to doubt the validity of spiritual healing myself; all the verbal expressions of principles and stories of successes were not making a dent. Consequently, we decided to have a healing service on Saturday night, allowing each of the doctors to bring in outsiders who needed healing to the closed session. We hoped a successful healing service would let everybody see first-hand what the experience is like.

We met in the chapel. The three of us prayed one at a time, so that everybody could witness each of us healing. The first subject was a doctor with three broken ribs. We prayed; nothing happened. We prayed some more; nothing happened. He kept pushing on his ribs, and they were getting worse, not better, probably because he was pushing on them so hard. Finally we dismissed him.

Then a little child with braces on her legs came and sat in the chair. We prayed for her, and nothing happened. And one after another came from 7 o'clock until about 9:30. It was beginning to look like one of those ultimate failures. In desperation, we decided to take a break and let everybody go into small groups. (When you don't know what else to do, put them in groups.)

There were five people there who wanted prayer for healing, but chose not to be on display to the assembly; so we took them in the back. One was a little child brought by his father, who angrily said, "Listen, we've been here since 7 o'clock. My child is tired and sleepy, and I'm disgusted. If you're going to pray, pray for him first so we can go on home." The little child was really a pitiful case. He had been through five major open-heart operations, including transplanting of veins from his arm into his chest cavity. The operations were successful, but the inside of his arm withered, so that one arm was much shorter than the other. Also, one side of his back was smaller than the other, and he was very dwarfed in size.

By this time, we were not much in a frame of mind to pray. Nevertheless, we had the other patients gather round, and we closed our eyes and we prayed for about 20 minutes. As we opened our eyes, the father held the little boy's hands out, and his arms appeared to be exactly the same length. In his excitement he ripped the buttons off the boy's shirt and he began to say, over and over, "My God, my God, I can't believe it. He's healed." Finally, he took the boy on home, and we took a break, feeling somewhat disappointed that this hadn't happened to one of the doctor's sons. Later, we prayed for the others in the group, but nothing spectacular happened.

We started Sunday by allowing everybody to share anything good that had come from the meeting. To our surprise, the little boy's father turned out to be one of the most prominent doctors in attendance. We weren't aware he was even a member of the group, because he had been sitting silently in the back of the auditorium all during the conference. Apparently, he was quite cynical about the medical profession after the failure of the operation on his son. Now, we heard this man relate his son's condition in scientific, medical terms, and he also described the experience of healing on the previous night. He said he stayed awake all night, and every 30 minutes he measured his son's arms and back to see if he retained the healing.

My Experiences During Healings

My own experiences during the healing process are difficult to describe. One would almost need to be in my body and mind to know what takes place. It is as though I am standing there looking on and listening to something happen, being as totally objective as I ever get. It seems that I have a gift of becoming disassociated from all emotion, although I become keenly sensitive to certain negative emotions. I can't seem to pinpoint what they are: they may be fear, or a sense of inferiority. I begin to feel sensation in certain parts of my body, and I know to keep my eyes on those same areas of the person's body. At the same time I'm talking, I feel almost suspended in time. Although a workshop will last four hours, it seems more like a few minutes. I experience no tiredness, no intense feelings, no emotion; just direct contact.

About two days after the workshop, when I am completely through with my work, and in a place where I can totally let down, then I begin to experience certain aftereffects. It's as though something is held somewhere intact until I can be free and let go, something like judgment being suspended. Things begin to surface in me. I never give a workshop without experiencing some healing of my own in some area. However, it's always delayed sometimes until I go off somewhere alone, usually in a cottage down by a lake. Sometimes the surfacing has happened to me on airplanes. It affects me in different ways: sometimes I want to cry; sometimes painful memories come up. I talk into a tape recorder, because it's almost a form of possession, and I choose not to communicate it to anyone other than myself. Sometimes I talk for three hours without stopping to a tape recorder.

I feel that many different methods in psychology enable us to get to the root causes of many illnesses and diseases; we can get at the facts about events that have happened. But it's not the *events* that caused the problem; it's the emotion that was repressed when the incident took place. That emotion is locked someplace in the unconscious. It's not easy to draw out and transform that emotion. A person may talk about it, may even recall it every day; but that still doesn't get rid of that emotion, because it's locked in.

In my idea of healing, the actual, unconditional love of Jesus has got to be communicated on the unconscious level to the person. Love is the healing agent. And the word "love" is used so loosely. I'm not talking about male-female love, erotic love, or even brotherly love. I'm talking about *creative energy love,* that dynamic love which to me is synonymous with the creative energy that raised Jesus from the dead. That kind of love—that power—is hard to communicate. But I believe that the best way is through direct contact with the Holy Spirit through Christ.

Discovering Unconditional Love

Christ is a lot of things to me. During the first 29 years of my life, He personified one who lived a life of testing, overcoming temptation and hardships, one who was the expression of love, and a great teacher. By faith, I assumed He was the Son of God, without any direct personal experience.

Then at the age of 29, for the first time in my life, I had the experience of unconditional love from and through a human being. When I met that psychologist who taught me to thank God for everything, he sensed a great hurt in me, a hurt that even I didn't know was there. I had never before shared any of the dark areas of my life, because I had always been a very closed person. I had never talked to anybody except superficially. At first, I refused to share any of this darkness with him; but he used the right psychological tools to open me up. Then, for about four to five hours, I talked unceasingly about every negative thing in my life, every unkind, unloving thing, every lie, every dark thing. I shared things just to shock him, not realizing that he was the one in charge. He was totally unaffected. Had any of this been known to my closed world of Christian friends, with their moralistic code of do's and don'ts, I would have felt judged and condemned. As it was, when I finished, he simply said, "I see how beautiful you are inside."

This attitude came out of a realm of thinking that I had never before experienced. I realized there are people who can see right through to beauty, never stopping to be aware of all the unhealed trash. That man was truly different from most people I had met. There was an element of the Christ in him, a loving, nonjudgmental nature, like the scripture where Paul says "Christ in me, the hope of glory." I then saw Jesus as One who can incarnate in human flesh through me, through you, through everybody. That was certainly a new dimension of Jesus for me.

It is extremely difficult to speak about Jesus and forget all of the conditionings and dogma associated with Christianity. To me, there's all the difference in the world between being a member of the Christian religion and being a Christ-like person. Jesus taught the principles of breaking down barriers. He was the one that went into the country of Samaria, which was forbidden to the

Jews; He reached out to the broken; He touched the unclean. I think He would have wanted to break down every barrier between every nation in the world, bringing unity among all people. Jesus never taught the kind of religious competition that has resulted in denominationalism. We as Christians have, in many ways, forgotten what He was teaching, the principles of love and honesty and integrity and forgiveness. He also urged us to go beyond what is justified in putting these principles into action, the concept of "going the extra mile." Many other great teachers have taught these same principles: truth is truth wherever you find it.

Forgiveness is the key to inner healing. Love is the key to inner healing. Affirmation is the key to inner healing. Many beautiful expressions in the scriptures directly pinpoint inner healing for me. I see the word "heart" as being synonymous with the unconscious. "I'll take that heart of stone and give to you, my people, a heart of flesh." "Let the words of your mouth and the meditations of your heart be the same." In my kind of inner healing, there is a root cause for every negative response that any human being experiences within. For each outburst of anger, there is a root cause. For every form of jealousy, there is a root cause. All types of sexual perversion have a root cause. There's very little that any of us do out of conscious, deliberate maliciousness. Even though our ugly actions may be conscious, they are motivated by a deep-seated, unconscious, uncontrollable expression of buried emotions. Jesus knew this; I see so much of His work as being psychological. When He said, "Before you take that speck out of another person's eye, take the plank out of your own eye," He knew that most of our view of evil is projection. We learn to be judgmental, rather than loving, at a very early age. It's not so much that we are verbally taught it, but our experiences of life are more painful than we're equipped to withstand. All the little hurts and rejections and putdowns that we have as little children make their indelible marks. Like most psychologists, I believe that, by the time we're five years old, the potential for all of our negative patterns has been formed in us.

new Dimensions
AUDIO JOURNAL

The **New Dimensions Audio Journal** is a quarterly 90-minute audio cassette tape publication covering the most exciting new ideas, choices, alternatives, options and solutions to appear in our time. With the **New Dimensions Audio Journal** you will actually listen to the sounds of transformation through the voices of many of the most respected and noted thinkers in science, health, psychology, personal growth, parapsychology, religion, social change, economics, ecology, the social sciences and the humanities. Hear them as they explore the farther reaches of the human body/mind/spirit.

You will come in touch with the nature of change in a most unique and dynamic way through the **New Dimensions Audio Journal**. Compiled and produced from the most stimulating and relevant material presented on New Dimensions Radio programs as well as other material never before released, the **Audio Journal** promises to be a listening adventure you won't want to miss. And of course in the process, you will be collecting an audio library that will give you untold hours of listening excitement, and will undoubtedly become even more historically important as time goes on.

Subscribe for $35 annually and receive a handsome vinyl binder to contain 4 cassette tape issues of the **Audio Journal**. Send your check or money order to **New Dimensions Audio Journal**, 267 States Street, San Francisco, California 94114.

new Dimensions Tapes

To enhance your experience of *The New Healers: Healing the Whole Person,* we offer these audio cassette tapes. Each of these programs presents rare and penetrating insights on the infinite panorama of human possibilities.

PATRICIA SUN I. Serves as an introduction to the work of the extraordinary teacher, who uses the vibrations of sound to reveal the spirit. (# 1085, 1 hr., $7.50)

PATRICIA SUN II. Here the joyful radiance and awareness of Patricia works as a catalyst to produce a dynamic experience for the listener. (# 1086, 1 hr., $7.50)

PATRICIA SUN, philosopher, human energizer and natural healer shows us ways to attain wholeness and gives us keys to bring more joy into our daily life. (# 1359, 1 hr., $7.50)

PATRICIA SUN / COMMUNICATION & CONSCIOUSNESS. The energy flows throughout this incredible presentation of how communication really works to actualize change. This is a rare glimpse into the nature of spontaneity and the transformation of energy. Moving and very special. (# 1129, 4 hrs., $30)

BIRTH WITHOUT VIOLENCE/ FREDERICK LEBOYER. A specially produced 1 hour program designed to portray the pioneering work of the French obstetrician, DR. FREDERICK LEBOYER. Leboyer has created a new way of bringing babies into the world, which this program illustrates through the words of Leboyer himself, what others have to say about his process and a touching description of a Leboyer birth. The purpose of the program is to call attention to this fresh and important perspective on the birth process, which is receiving worldwide acclaim. (#1038, 1 hr., $7.50)

LOVING HANDS/BEING BORN. FREDERICK LEBOYER II. Here the author of *Birth Without Violence* and *Loving Hands* talks about his supremely simple approach to loving in the here and now. (# 1062, 1 hr., $7.50)

FREDERICK LEBOYER REVISITED. The world renowned French obstetrician who pioneered "Birth Without Violence," talks about new ways to live in the spirit. (# 1388, 1 hr., $7.50)

THE NEW MEDICINE: HOLISTIC HEALTH, PART I. Panacea or problem box? An incisive look at the roots of the holistic model and how it blends or competes with the more traditional allopathic system. Includes conversations with numerous holistic health practitioners and insights about homeopathy, herbology, body/mind disciplines, natural childbirth, the politics of health, life-death transitions and much more. Guests include CHARLES GARFIELD, founder of the Shanti Project; ALAN NELSON, consulting director of the Holistic Health Institute; RICHARD MILES, coordinator of Healthnet; KEN DYCHTWALD, author of *Bodymind.* (#1367, 2 hrs., $15)

THE NEW MEDICINE: HOLISTIC HEALTH, PART II. (#1368, 2 hrs., $15)

DR· IRVING OYLE & DARLA CHADIMA. A look at what the New Age is and is not. What the future holds for the New Age Movement(s). (#1362, 2 hrs., $15)

To order tapes send check or money order including 50¢ packaging and handling fee for each tape title to: New Dimensions Tapes, 267 States Street, San Francisco, California 94114 (California residents add 6% sales tax).

new Dimensions Tapes

To enhance your experience of *The New Healers: Healing the Whole Person,* we offer these audio cassette tapes. Each of these programs presents rare and penetrating insights on the infinite panorama of human possibilities.

MOSHE FELDENKRAIS the author of AWARENESS THROUGH MOVEMENT shares his vision, warmth and wisdom in dicussing life and human nature. (# 1170, 2 hrs., $15)

LINUS PAULING. The two-time Nobel prize-winner on vitamin C, cancer, the common cold, and how to be well. (# 1174, 2 hrs., $15)

HAROLD BLOOMFIELD. Co-author of *TM* and *Happiness.* (# 1083, 1 hr., $7.50)

JUDITH MC KINNON I. MASSAGE & HEALTH with JUDITH MC KINNON. Massage artist, talks about energy, breath, visualizations and the experience of a healthy body. (# 1257, 1½ hrs., $12)

THE PSYCHIC JOURNEY/JACK SCHWARZ. Alive and filled with inspiration, this conversation with Schwarz, the acknowledged master of voluntary control of internal states, is both amazing and revealing for its profound spiritual insight. (# 1052, 1½ hrs., $12)

JACK SCHWARZ/LIVING NOW. The master teacher and healer presents in a remarkably clear manner just what we need to do to get on with our lives. Lucid & loaded. (# 1127, 1 hr. 45 min., $15)

JACK SCHWARZ III. Author of *The Path of Action* and *Voluntary Controls,* talks about personal change and evolution in ways that open doors for everyone. (# 1238, 2 hrs., $15)

JACK SCHWARZ IV. Talks about living in the moment and how to get the most out of life by realizing our true potential. (# 1372, 1 hr., $7.50)

HEALING THE WHOLE PERSON. Dimensions of healing are explored and new alternatives examined. From sonic acupuncture to Ki energy, DR. IRVING OYLE, author of *The Healing Mind,* RALPH METZNER, author of *Maps of Consciousness,* JOSH CARTER, iridologist and optometrist and others share present reality and future visions of health. Also includes: ALLAN COHEN, HILLERY ANDERSON, ALAN SHIFMAN, KHALED AL-FAKIH, KIM MC KELL. (# 1047, 4 hrs., $30)

CHARLES GARFIELD/COMPASSION FOR LIFE . A New view for the dying experience. CHARLES GARFIELD founding director of the Shanti Project, a volunteer counseling service for the dying and their families, looks at death and dying, one of the major hang-ups of our society. (# 1033, 1½ hrs., $12)

RUTH CARTER STAPLETON. The spiritual healer talks about the nature of inner healing in a warm and enlightening conversation. (# 1313, 2 hrs., $15)

SPIRITUAL HEALING. THE NON-RATIONAL APPROACH TO PERSONAL HEALTH. An overview of how the realm of the spirit relates to the domain of health. PATRICIA SUN is the capstone climax to a circular discussion including DR. CARL SIMONTON, J. RICHARD TURNER, DR. RICHARD SVHUS, DON CARTER and others. Includes an actual healing. Also includes: Schawkie Roth, Pat Fearey, Rev. Plume & Walter Hogue, Pam Rassmussen, Rev. Beneit, Jerry Berg & Jocelyn Townsend. (#1049, 4 hrs., $30)

To order tapes send check or money order including 50¢ packaging and handling fee for each tape title to: New Dimensions Tapes, 267 States Street, San Francisco, California 94114 (California residents add 6% sales tax).